From Horizontal To Vertical

Working with paralysed people in Bangladesh

By Corinna Thomas

Foreword by Mark Tully

All royalties from this book will go directly to the charity
FRIENDS OF THE CENTRE
FOR THE REHABILITATION OF THE PARALYSED
(FCRP)

Available from:

> Summersdale Publishers
> PO Box 49
> Chichester
> PO19 4LF
> UK

A CIP catalogue record for this book is available from the British Library.

ISBN 1 873475 01 2

Reprinted 1993

Cover design by Chloe Sitwell

Printed in Great Britain by
Antony Rowe Ltd, Chippenham, Wiltshire

Acknowledgements

I would like to thank the following people:

Valerie Taylor, for everything.

Wendy Best and Holly Makin, for their contributions and photographs.

Peter Hunt, for filling in the gaps.

Begum Hosneara, for help and advice regarding language and cultural points.

Walter Holt, for his photographs.

Chloe Sitwell, for her brilliant cover design.

For Valerie

"Valerie Taylor gives paralysed people hope and the will to live. She enables them to go back to their families, often in villages, not as dependants, not as burdens, but as breadwinners in their own right."

Sir Terence Streeton KCMG,

British High Commissioner to Bangladesh (1983-1989)

Contents

Foreword - by Mark Tully	7
Introduction	10
The Plunge	11
The Founder	19
In At The Deep End	24
Basketball on Wheels	31
Apni Bangla Bolte Paren? (Do you speak Bengali?)	38
Second Week Blues	42
Time Out	52
The Masochist Marathon	58
Hold my Hand	62
Cooking Pot Commode	70
Goats' Visiting Hours	78
Code of Conduct	84
Cockroaches - the Night of the Long Knives	94
A Rusty Introduction to Nursing	100
A Pint of Blood	106
Eyes on a Streaming Face	111
The Gold of Bangladesh	118
Joyti and Poppy	123
Old Dhaka on a Motorbike	129
Reflections	134
The Future	140
Epilogue	144
Bibliography	151

Foreword

By Mark Tully
BBC India Correspondent

When Bangladesh broke away from Pakistan after nine months of bloody civil war, Henry Kissinger described it as "a basket case". More than twenty years and many millions of pounds of aid later that's the way the country is still seen by officials of those governments which give that aid. A bucket with a hole in the bottom might be a better description of the aid donors' view because so much money has been poured into Bangladesh and yet, in their view, so little has been achieved. Who should be blamed? According to far too many officials and journalists the Bangladeshis. Every evening in the drawing room of diplomatic Dhaka the conversation turns to the corruption of Bangladesh, to the large sums of money aid donors 'generously' donate that get diverted to the pockets of politicians and middlemen. I must say, however, that I do remember one American diplomat in Dhaka saying to me "We don't have much to congratulate ourselves on, after all we can afford not to be corrupt." But that apart in Dhaka I am all too often reminded of Victorian Britain where all except the most enlightened thought "the poor will always be with us", and regarded them as lazy, drunken, immoral, and thoroughly deserving of their fate. A little charity, from the pocket not the heart of course, was all most Victorians thought they owed the poor of their own country.

History has shown that charity does not work. It was not until the poor in Britain found a political voice of their own in this century that radical changes took place in our society. In the same way so long as the poor countries remain bit-part actors on the international stage with all the lead roles being taken by the rich, they too will not get their rights but have to depend on charity, which can at best help bind some of the wounds of late twentieth century capitalism.

Of course in the many years that I have been reporting on

Bangladesh I have met many foreigners who do understand the country, and treat its problems as their own. Most of them worked for voluntary agencies, and it is a hopeful sign that the governments who give aid are now paying more attention to the recommendations of the voluntary agencies and involving them in projects too. But the voluntary agencies are not wealthy or powerful enough to change the world, and that's what really is required if countries like Bangladesh are to prosper.

Corinna Thomas' description of the work of the Centre for the Rehabilitation of the Paralysed can leave no one in any doubt about the changes in the lives of individual Bangladeshis which voluntary organisations can and do make. Just to give one example, there is the story of when Shotorbabu sang again because he realised that life after a stroke could still have meaning. When he suffered that stroke he said he would never sing again. But at the same time Corinna Thomas vividly describes Bangladeshi government hospital treatment, thus making it clear that, thoroughly admirable although the work of the Centre undoubtedly is, it has not made a major impact on medical services throughout the country. But this book's impact could be much wider if it inspires other young people in the richer countries to go out and learn by their own experience how unfair the world is still.

Corinna Thomas is a remarkably wise guide for those who want to follow her example. She tried, obviously with considerable success, not to be shocked by the poverty, to see the poor as individual people not as some terrifying phenomenon. She did not patronise, but showed respect for Bengali culture, even when a policeman reprimanded her for what back home would certainly not be considered any sort of offence. She laughed at herself, particularly her difficulty in eating with only one hand, rather than laughing at Bangladeshi customs. She left behind Bangladeshis who knew that she was not just another foreigner she was someone who cared deeply for them and their country.

When Corinna Thomas was thinking about her "Year Off" she had "this heroic (though certainly not unique) notion of saving the world." After reading this book I'm quite certain that she no longer has such unrealistic ambitions, but I hope that something of that dream remains. I hope she will continue to try to influence her own generation so that they insist that poverty is put at the top of the international political agenda, and that the rights of the poor are respected, that they are treated as people who are owed something more than charity.

She has already made an impact on one member of an older generation. After reading her unaffected and humorous diary I realise how much I have missed by reporting on the poor rather than working with them. In all the time I have spent in Dhaka I have not even visited Valerie Taylor, who is the heroine of this book, and her Centre for the Rehabilitation of the Paralysed. That at least is one omission I will put right.

Introduction

Short term or visiting volunteers have been part of the family of the Centre for the Rehabilitation of the Paralysed (CRP) in Bangladesh for many years now. They play a very important part of that ever increasing family as they not only help 'on the spot' in Bangladesh but assist in creating interest and raising funds once they return to their home countries.

Our visiting volunteers come with a variety of experiences in life. They range from college students, with their youthful enthusiasm and sense of adventure, to trained therapists, with their specialised expertise, to people (too many to list) who have worked for the British Film Industry, the BBC, an antique dealer, a retired post-master, a teacher, a housewife to name but a few. We feel that everyone has a part to play whether it be cutting toenails, trimming beards, playing Ludo or wheelchair basket-ball, repairing vehicles or equipment or giving of their nursing, physiotherapy or occupational therapy skills.

Without fail, when it is time for a volunteer to leave us, apart from the practical help we have received, the fun we have shared, we are conscious that the Centre has gained a new friend. I believe this is what it is all about - sharing experiences, deepening understanding and thereby forging new friendships.

Thanks to Corinna's great enthusiasm, interest and affection for paralysed people in Bangladesh she has set down something of her experiences as a volunteer for all to share. We are most grateful to her.

Long may the visiting volunteer continue as part of the CRP's family, where hopefully as a result of the experience all sides will benefit.

Valerie Taylor.
17. 1. 92

Chapter I

The Plunge

If someone had told me during the dark days of exam revision that I would come through the whole stressful period and go to work for three months in a hospital in Bangladesh, I would have thought they were crazy. But soon everyone returned to school from their Easter holidays in far off and exotic lands looking tanned and healthy and as if they had done no work, this sparked off the beginnings of wild and fantastic dreams of travel. However, A-levels were now lurking ominously in the not-too-distant future, so I tried to push these ideas to the back of my mind and do some work.

As the term wore on my friends started to receive replies from the various universities and other forms of further education to which they had applied. Whenever my pile of work grew too large I had wandered down to the careers room, but instead of leafing through the millions of prospectuses I went straight to the shelf labelled 'Year Off'. After all, a year off is an important part of further education. It was easier to think about travelling to exciting places than to question my academic future. I knew that I did not want to go straight from school into more years of lectures without a break, and I also had this heroic (though certainly not unique) notion of saving the world.

With these thoughts firmly lodged in my mind I applied to Voluntary Service Overseas (VSO), and several other well known big organisations. I did not hold out much hope and consequently was not surprised when they wrote back informing me that I had to be two years older and qualified in a field that would benefit the developing world. Some of the projects also asked each volunteer to pay a large sum towards their living costs once out there, they seemed to be asking for a great deal, more than I would have been able to raise.

I have suffered from foot problems all my life and when I spent three weeks in hospital recovering from an operation on both feet I begun to appreciate how vital mobility is in life. I think it is impossible to really feel what it is like to be disabled unless you are so yourself but I do believe that the three weeks of total bed-rest that I experienced gave me a good insight to the difficulties that any paralysed person would encounter. What ever it was that I gained from my stay in hospital I realised that I wanted to help the vast immobile population.

My first opportunity came in the sixth form when I signed up to do voluntary work in the local vicinity. I was asked to visit an elderly man who had just had his leg amputated and to keep him company during the long afternoons. We did not need any introductions because Bob used to work in the junior school and remembered me from the days when we all used to beg for some of his sweet tea. Bob had only recently been discharged from the ward environment and was beginning the slow and painful process of learning to live with his disability. I used to take Bob out in his wheelchair so that he could enjoy the fresh air and countryside which were otherwise beyond his reach. Bob often said that he felt like a prisoner in his own home and felt humiliated by having to have help in doing the most mundane activities such as having a shower, which he had been doing without a second's thought for over sixty years. Bob made a steady recovery and now walks with an artificial leg and can drive a special car, both of which have been supplied by the council.

Bob reintroduced me to his son Neil, who at the age of nineteen had a motorbike accident and broke his neck. I say 'reintroduced' because when I was in the junior school we all raised money to buy Neil an electric wheelchair. Nine years on I wanted Neil's advice on my design A-level project which was to design and build a motored page turner for the disabled. I had chosen this project so that in my own small way I could try to help those less fortunate than myself. Neil seemed the perfect person to help me because not only could he try it out at each stage and provide constructive criticism, he was also on every committee in the south of the country campaigning for better living conditions for the disabled. Neil arranged for me to see other disabled people who all had homes full of the most up to date equipment but had never found an affordable page turner that worked properly. I was also able to work closely with the elderly and severely arthritic people who were all extremely encouraging about my enthusiasm and work, despite it being on such a simple level. It was during this time that I thought of nursing as a career.

By this time I had set my heart on the idea of doing some voluntary work abroad and was quite upset at the thought that I would never get the opportunity. My hopes were heightened while I was trying to revise for my mocks when I received a letter from my father in Bangladesh. He told me that he had just participated in a wheelchair race to raise money for an amazing hospital run by an English physiotherapist. My father had always said that he could see me as the second Pauline Cutting (a doctor who worked in dangerous conditions in Beirut) and suggested that I wrote to the project coordinator. My geography notes were forgotten immediately and I wrote off to Valerie Taylor, expecting her reply to be as negative as all of the others - after all, why would anyone want to be responsible for an unskilled eighteen year old miles away from home for three months?

My school was offering six places to students to go to Africa to teach in small schools during their year off, but despite the negative responses I was getting from trying to arrange something on my own I did not even try for one of the places. I knew that I wasn't cut out to be a teacher and wanted to persevere with the hospital line. When I received the letter from my father I was especially thrilled because not only was there a chance of work in a hospital, but also it specialised in spinal injuries - the only field of health in which I had any experience.

When I opened the reply from Valerie I could not believe my luck as I read her words of enthusiasm and warmth: she was welcoming me to her centre at any time. I was so excited that the entire school knew of my news before the day was out. Until that day, to me Bangladesh had just been a country associated with natural disasters talked about on the news. All I knew was that it often flooded and is near India. Now that I had replied to Valerie saying that I would spend three months in her centre helping in anyway that I could I thought I had better learn a little about the country and its people.

I found an Atlas and saw that Bangladesh is surrounded by India to the west, north-west and east. The south-eastern border is with

Burma and to the south is the Bay of Bengal. There are one hundred and ten million people living in Bangladesh, a country only the size of England and Wales. It is the most densely populated country in the world. Eighty per cent of the population live below the poverty line, and less than twenty per cent are literate. A staggering ninety percent live in rural Bangladesh yet eighty five percent of the population are landless. Officially Bangladesh is the second poorest nation in the world after Bhutan. Nearly ninety per cent of the country's development budget is provided by foreign aid.

All of these facts and figures did not put me off. Rather, they made me want to go and experience it for myself. At some stage I did revise for my A' levels and managed to get them all - just! I won a travel award from my school but it was not enough for my flight, let alone my expenses, so I went to live with my parents in Bulgaria and worked in the Anglo-American school. I worked as a teacher aid in the pre-school, which was a class of twenty international children. In the afternoons I au-paired for two boys. After four months I had earnt and saved enough money to finance my trip.

I had been advised to allow a budget of £1 a day for food and travel plus whatever my accommodation might cost (which could be anything between £0.50 to £75 depending on the conditions in which I was prepared to live).

While I was busy teaching four year olds how to paint pretty pictures, my brother kindly researched ticket prices to Bangladesh. He found that the best bargain was not on the direct flight with Biman (Bangladeshi airline) but with Air India to Delhi and then Indian Airlines to Dhaka via Calcutta. I ended up paying £450 for the return ticket. I applied for a tourist visa, which was granted for three months with no trouble at all. Problems can arise if you want to stay for a longer period of time or if you state that you are going to do any form of work. But once in the country it is usually easy to get an extension.

I had a few days in London during which I rushed around like a mad hatter buying up the entire contents of Boots. This included exciting things such as water purification tablets, most of which came home with me three months later. I went to my GP and came away feeling like a pin cushion. I had to have a polio and tetanus booster and I needed a health certificate to show to the immigration officer in Dhaka, stating that I had had inoculations for cholera and typhoid. I also had the Gamma Globulin inoculation against infectious hepatitis. I was advised to have the nasty human-diploid cell rabies vaccine, but as the course takes one month to complete I had to forgo it. I was later to regret this when I discovered that a pack of wild dogs were living outside my home, and they all looked hungrier each day. The malaria-carrying mosquitoes are only supposed to exist in the Chittagong Hill Tracts in the south-east but I decided to be on the safe side and take a chloroquine tablet every day.

I said goodbye to my anxious parents and jealous brother and sister before bravely stepping through the departure barrier at Heathrow airport. I began to think of or at least try to visualise what lay ahead of me, but, nervously clutching my return ticket, no clear thoughts appeared. I was surrounded by fellow western travellers on the flight to Delhi, but once inside the terminal for internal flights I was abandoned. This was a great shame as I then had to face a fourteen hour delay, which did nothing to soothe my nerves. The available amenities consisted of one tap, which dribbled unsafe water, and one blocked loo. Besides which I had to sit on a hard seat in a deserted room with my back pack firmly tied to my leg.

During another six hour delay in Calcutta I met a fellow Westerner. I did not have time to finish explaining why I was heading for Dhaka, for as soon as I mentioned the word 'centre' my new friend said I could only be going to The Centre For The Rehabilitation Of The Paralysed, run by Valerie. I was so happy to have met someone with whom I could communicate, and to encounter a fan of Valerie's was a real bonus. I was assured that I would not want to use my return ticket in three months time. I prayed that he was right, but at that very moment I was more worried by the prospect of arriving at two in the morning on my own.

Apart from Derek I was the only white person on the twenty minute flight to Dhaka. I had left the well trodden paths of India and was heading for a country that very few tourists or travellers visit. Bangladesh has yet to trap and accommodate the tourist market, but a great deal of money is being put into the tourist industry. And there is huge potential, particularly considering it has the longest sandy beach in the world, measuring seventy miles.

Forty hours after leaving London I did arrive in Dhaka, but I was not alone for longer than it took to get through the immigration barrier. My mind was immediately put at rest when I saw a lone woman waiting and instantly knew it was Valerie. She had been at the airport for six hours but could only express her concern about how tired I must have been. A totally selfless attitude is Valerie all over. The centre's ambulance was waiting outside and we set off for the VSO guest house without even having to push start it - this was taken to be a good sign for my stay. Our journey was made in the dark so I was unable to get any bearings.

I lived in India until I was four years old and apparently had more Indian characteristics than English. Although I do not remember my childhood days in Delhi I think they must have helped as I did not suffer from culture shock as many Westerners do. Back home I had been advised to dye my blonde hair black so that I would not be hassled by pawing men, and was also told to wear a headscarf with a veil at all times, Bangladesh being a Muslim country. Although I made no such drastic changes to my appearance, I did always keep my shoulders and legs covered, and that was fine. As long as foreigners respect the Bengali's culture the Bengalis will respect them.

In the morning I was met by the hospital's messenger who had been sent for me so that I would not yet have to work out how to use the public transport. Valerie thought it best that I should have a few days to grow accustomed to my new surroundings. I was given a helmet and invited to jump onto the back of the motorbike. With a big mischievous smile on his face Khokon wove his way through chaotic traffic that made Piccadilly Circus in rush hour seem tame. We narrowly missed stray cows, goats and packs of dogs; not to mention the thousands of roaming people who seemed oblivious to the oncoming traffic. I kept on thinking how pleased I was that I was in the relatively safe position of the back seat and with a helmet on. Khokon screamed out to me that Bengali women will not wear crash helmets, which made him very cross.

One of the first things I noticed were the colours in the general street scenes. All of the cycle rickshaws and motored babytaxis have bright pictures painted on the hoods and each one tells a tale of a famous actress or a mythical figure. Wherever I looked I saw crowds, and everyone seemed to be going about their own business, taking little interest in others. The exception to this was if anything stood in their way, and then they would shout and curse at the offending person or object. The result made Dhaka a very noisy city, for added to the shouts of people were the never ending blasts from horns of impatient drivers in exotic vehicles.

Green Road, Central Dhaka
This is a typical street scene of rickshaws,
babytaxis and tempos.

It is impossible not to notice the poverty in Dhaka. Although I was not shocked or offended by it, it did make me realise how much we take for granted back at home. We passed deformed figures abandoned on the street begging for a few taka, and groups of children calling out "Baksheesh" (asking for money) on every corner. I caught glimpses of market stalls on the pavements selling a few grains of rice, and cigarettes were sold by the one instead of the packet. It is a country of such aesthetic paradoxes as beautiful bunches of flowers being sold by an old man squatting over an open sewer. These sewers usually ran along the roadside. Children dug deep into the bins to see if there was anything worth salvaging to help fill their empty stomachs or keep them warm at night.

A worrying thought passed through my mind: who was I to think I could arrive in Bangladesh, stay for three months doing 'good work' and then just leave to return to my own safe world? I felt I was being unduly patronising, especially as I had no trade or training with which to help this poor nation. Surely I must see myself as ultimately superior. I realised that all voluntary and aid workers could be looked upon in such a way, but if each individual carries out their work in an understanding, helpful and human way they need not be. I tried to think positively, reassuring myself that I was not superior, just a willing person with a spare pair of hands.

Finally a footbridge came in sight. I knew that we must have been close to the centre because I had been told that the bridge marked the beginning of the area called Farmgate, where the centre was situated. We turned into the drive and I nimbly hopped off the motorbike and braced myself for the beginning of my three month stint.

Chapter 2

The Founder

Valerie Taylor spent three years of her youth in Argentina where her father was a medical missionary. Back in England, her country of birth, Valerie became interested in the idea of becoming a doctor. But despite trying her hardest she could not fulfil her aim because she failed physics three times.

"I wanted to be a doctor but wasn't clever enough: physiotherapy seemed the next best thing, " she told me. Valerie was accepted into the physiotherapy course at St. Thomas' Hospital.

Valerie had always been interested in south-east Asia and became more so when she read a book on the setting up of a hospital near Madras in India. She was so taken by the idea that she applied to VSO. In October of 1969 Valerie was sent to East Pakistan as a volunteer physiotherapist. Valerie began by dividing her day between a Christian hospital and a leprosy hospital, both of which were situated in Chandraghona near the Burmese border in the Chittagong Hill Tracts. Valerie set up a small physiotherapy centre in the general hospital where she treated polio cases and victims of accidents from the local paper mill, as well as general problems and the leprosy sufferers.

In March 1971 the War of Independence began. The Pakistan army cracked down on the autonomist forces who were demanding an immediate transfer of power to the party in East Pakistan. There was mass killing in Dhaka and elsewhere in the country. Valerie was in the middle of cutting up a pair of crutches when she received a message from the British Council ordering her to evacuate. Valerie felt cross that her day's work had been interrupted, but did as she was told and joined all of the other British expatriates and was evacuated to Bangkok. Valerie could not wait until liberation was announced and returned to Chandraghona in November 1971. It was not until December 16th that liberation day came and the country Bangladesh was born.

Valerie trained a man from the Chakma tribe (one of twenty

different tribes situated in the Chittagong Hill Tracts) to become her assistant and together they worked in primitive conditions with limited equipment. Valerie treated only four paralysed people, all of whom had been involved in accidents at the local paper mill. She became very involved with her four patients but did not feel happy about the level of treatment she was able to give to them.

"I thought it was wrong to take these people into hospital just to prolong their lives by a few months. There was nothing for them to go home to - they would either beg or rot to death. There were no wheelchairs, no means of income, no real care. " It was whilst administering care for these four patients that the turning point came for Valerie, and she realised that she wanted to branch away from general physiotherapy and specialise in spinal injuries.

Valerie spent the years 1973 to 1975 in England, devoting her time to trying to persuade organisations to help her finance her plan to form a centre for the rehabilitation of the paralysed. No one seemed interested. But when Valerie contacted the Christopel Blindon Mission they told her about a new project started by the Bengali government. They had opened a vocational retraining and job replacement department and she was advised to join them rather than to try and duplicate their work. Valerie had been happy with VSO, and so applied again and returned to Bangladesh in 1975.

Working in the new department Valerie tried to retrain her patients in order to find them jobs. But despite her efforts she found that many of her patients would never leave their hospital beds. Valerie quickly realised the need to take these people away from a hospital environment, but she also knew that the government would be slow and reluctant to change things.

1976 saw the graduation of the first Bangladeshi physiotherapists ever to be trained to degree level. Valerie sat down with a physiotherapist, occupational therapist and a social worker and discussed her idea of starting again as a separate project. The main problem with the government hospital was that Valerie and her colleagues were scheduled only to work hard through the day, from early morning to mid-afternoon. This meant that from three o'clock in the afternoon until the next morning none of their patients were seen to - none were turned over, and they were more often than not simply left to lie in a wet and dirty bed. The team were working against a vicious circle.

Valerie spent the next two years campaigning to raise money for the new centre. With the help of Oxfam, other charities and generous individuals, she raised enough money to start her dream centre. It took another year before Valerie was given permission to convert some old store rooms in the hospital into a centre with six beds. Valerie made this big step in Bangladeshi health care not a moment too soon, as the last physiotherapy students had graduated the year before in 1978. Out of the thirty one graduates nineteen went abroad leaving one physiotherapist per nine million people.

In December 1981 the government required the space that the centre was occupying for their own hospital staff. The centre was forced to make its first move to another rented building in Dhaka. The number of beds in the centre had increased to thirty-five before it had to move again in 1986. On the day of the move there was a general strike which meant that the hired lorries never arrived to transport all of the contents from the second to the third hospital. Consequently each patient was wheeled down Green Road with a parcel of their personal belongings on their laps. The two sites were a good two miles from each other.

Everyone and everything crammed into a two storey house in Farmgate and Valerie managed to rent a tiny piece of extra land at the back for all of the workshops. It was at this site that I found them in January 1990.

Others often describe Valerie as a saint or the second Mother Theresa but she herself disagrees. "I don't regard myself as a saint, the work is so rewarding. I am very conscious of other people's interest and support. I get so much satisfaction in tiny ways. I know it is all worthwhile when I see a paralysed person smile and want to fight back."

Creating the centre was not enough for Valerie, even though she worked from sunrise to sunset,

"I was leading a very selfish life and decided to share my room with a child who needed love and a home. Valerie did not think she could provide a proper home or family to an able bodied child, and wanted to help someone less fortunate. Valerie became the legal guardian to a little five year old girl, (the most precise the workers at the orphanage could be as no one knew her actual birth date), who suffered from cerebral palsy and had been abandoned by her parents. Cerebral Palsy covers a variety of disorders caused by brain damage which occurs before, during or soon after birth. It is not curable. Joyti was not only given a home but also an extremely loving and qualified mother who worked hard with her.

Joyti, now fifteen, can walk using a special high walking frame, is bilingual in Bengali and English, and attends a normal school. When Joyti was eleven Valerie became the legal guardian to another cerebral palsy victim, a small girl of two who suffered from the disease very badly and has spastic paralysis. Again Valerie put all of her spare time into helping Poppy improve, which she has done with considerable speed. Poppy's story resembles the one of Christie Brown portrayed in the film 'My Left Foot' in that she is now learning to pick things up and turn pages with her left foot. Poppy cannot control her arms at all and has less control of her right foot than the left. Now aged six Poppy attends a Bengali govern-ment-run school for children with special needs. Both girls are always smiling and were often in the grounds of the centre chatting away to patients and staff alike, or could be found getting up to mischief with their au-pair in the staff quarters where Valerie and the two kids shared a single room.

Valerie Taylor, Joyti and Poppy

When Valerie is not working she concentrates on giving them physiotherapy as well as doing the things that any mother enjoys with her kids. The adoption law was abolished in Bangladesh before Valerie took in Joyti. This was unfortunate as she would like to be more than their legal guardian, though the children never think about what her role in law is to them - they just think of and love her as their mother.

Valerie once said to me,

"They are both beautiful children, so bright and happy and full of fun. It's a real pleasure to have such wonderful company." I cannot think of a better sentence to sum up the Taylor family of three.

Chapter 3

In At The Deep End

The few glimpses I had of Dhaka on the way into the centre from the back of the motorbike left an impression of hustle and bustle that was like nothing I had seen before. On entering the centre my impressions did not change. We walked through the front garden where a few patients sat around chatting to each other near the empty pond. A small child played happily on the stone statue of a lion by the front door. A distressed family were comforting each other on the front porch: their son had just been admitted after crashing his lorry and his prognosis was not good.

I was struck by the grandeur of the building, with its marble tiled floors, high ceilings and white painted walls. Khokon explained to me that it used to be the home of a rich land owner and was the grandest building in the area. But the landlord wanted the centre out by March, one of the reasons being because the wheelchairs were slowly ruining the interior.

On entering the centre I experienced a wave of nausea brought on by the lingering stench of urine, faeces and open wounds. The corridor seemed dark and empty, but I did not feel quite up to poking my head into the main ward as I walked past. I was relieved when we turned the corner and came out onto an open verandah, which ran along the entire side of the building and into the female ward. I was pointed into the office where a dozen people were clustered. At first it looked like a coffee morning was in progress: several people were holding out mugs for some of Valerie's never ending black tea, and some were passing round the tin of biscuits which make up a large percentage of the staff's daily intake of food. Everyone stopped talking and waited for Khokon to introduce me. There were lot of nervous giggles when poor Khokon tried to pronounce my name so I told everyone to call me by my shortened name, Rin.

Then it was my turn to turn scarlet as I tried to repeat all the names of everyone as they introduced themselves. Robbie was simple enough - he was the occupational therapist. Then there was Rhoman the physiotherapist and Hosneara the female physiotherapist. The two social workers introduced themselves as Salam and Farid and then I extended my hand across the table to Mohua, the centre's secretary, who is one of the five disabled members of staff. I was handed a cup of tea and a pile of sweet biscuits and made to feel at home straight away. The staff had all heard about my horrendous journey and had gathered to meet me on arrival. Mohua said that she was surprised that I had come in so early and smiled when I replied that I could not wait any longer having come this far.

Mohua had come down with a disease called Transverse Myelitis when she was a child in her teens. It is a crippling disease of the spinal cord, and very little is known as to how it develops. Like the majority of the victims of this cruel disease, Mohua caught a fever and went to bed one night feeling weak and woke up the next morning unable to move her legs. She has not had any feeling in them to this day.

I heard Valerie shout hello, but could not make out where she was. Seeing my puzzled look Robbie laughed and told me she was in her office behind the huge pile of boxes and added that he would not be surprised if one day she was found under the pile of fast accumulating papers, boxes and general junk. Valerie's office could easily be mistaken for a cupboard, and an untidy one at that. But despite the chaos Valerie can always clear a tiny space on the desk to reply to each donor or well-wisher, not to mention run the centre.

I already knew that the majority of patients with broken necks had been carrying a heavy weight on their head and slipped on wet mud or tripped on the uneven surface underfoot. The weight shifts and falls on the back of the neck. Luckily we hardly ever see this in England because we realise the potential dangers of carrying heavy loads on our heads, even if it does not slip the sheer weight can damage the delicate spine. In the UK a colossal number of working days are lost from bad backs but in Bangladesh the people grind on with their work until they literally snap because they can not afford to loose a days pay. The most common cause of broken backs are from falls out of trees while harvesting coconuts and other tree grown crops and falling from electricity poles and roof tops.

Victims who are left paralysed from traffic accidents and fevers are also treated in the centre although the number of cases is considerably less. The very causes of the accidents help to illustrate the level of development that Bangladesh is currently in. I had also been informed that the average length of stay in the centre is six months, the time it takes to rehabilitate someone physically, psychologically and financially.

I was let loose to wander around until someone was free to give me a proper guided tour. Thankfully I had only got as far as the end of the verandah when Glen came bounding up to show me around very quickly. Glen originally came to Bangladesh to start up a workshop for the production of artificial limbs. He trained Bengalis to make the limbs out of resources available, but in between the courses he helped out at the centre in the metal workshop. He had been at the centre on and off for three years and knew all there is to know about walking aids, callipers and back braces (which are just a few of the things that the centre makes on site).

I could hear the animals before we saw them in a pen that was raised up on stilts. A small boy was busy feeding the goats and chickens and had carefully balanced three eggs on his trolley bed beside him. Glen introduced me to Mr Topi, a name given to the boy because he always wore a little knitted hat throughout the year. I was left alone with Mr Topi for a few minutes while Glen went to sort out a small commotion, which as far as I could make out was an argument between two patients as to whose turn it was to practice walking on the parallel bars.

With a combination of my ridiculous sign language and his limited English I established that patients take it in turns to feed the animals, collect the eggs and to clean the pen. The idea behind this scheme is to teach the patients how to care for animals from a wheelchair - something which plays an important role in rural life.

I later discovered that a special short tree called Napier is grown along the garden wall. It has very nutritious leaves and is fast-growing. For the same reason a certain type of grass is also grown. It was not an unusual sight to see patients cutting the grass in the morning with a hand scythe before feeding time. Abdus B Salam was particularly keen on this job just as he was always ready to give a hand tending the orchids. Salam could walk with a stiff stride but was in considerable pain from a tumour at the top of his spine. Nevertheless he often helped out other patients who were worse off than himself.

I could see the frame which held all of the orchids, and saw they were just green plants being mid January which was a pity because when in flower they are beautiful brightly coloured plants. The orchid production began a few years back when a set of bulbs were given as a gift. Ever since they have been propagated and consequently have multiplied into many varieties. At the right time of year the frame cannot be seen for the mass of different coloured flowers. As well as giving pleasure to the patients and adding some colour to the otherwise dreary back yard, the flowers are sold for a relatively large sum of money to the big hotels.

Both the wood and metal workshops are accommodated in the yard, along with the physiotherapy department which consists of a tin-roofed shelter with no sides, apart from the garden wall.

Walking back past the bathsheds I seemed to be the only person not doing anything. A care assistant was wheeling a bare body on a metal trolley into one of the two showers and a man was wheeling himself along in his bulky wheelchair into the toilet. He had opted for the western style toilet which is easier to use if a patient can stand but not squat. There are also the Asian hole-in-the-floor types, over which a wheelchair can be placed so that a paralysed person need not even get out of his wheelchair which has a hole cut in the seat which is normally covered by a padded cushion.

On my left along the wall of the covered verandah lay three men in special beds known as Striker beds. They are designed to turn a patient over from a prone position (lying flat on the stomach) to a supine position (flat on the back) without actually moving the patient so as not to disturb the healing process of the spinal cord. The most serious cases have to spend six long weeks in one of these beds at the beginning of their treatment: these are usually people who have broken their neck.

It works like this: first of all a vicious-looking pair of skeletal tongs have to be screwed into the skull. The tongs have a weight attached to them which prevents any movement in the fragile neck. Every two hours a person who is unable to move himself has to be turned over to prevent the development of pressure sores, which can kill. Pressure sores develop where constant pressure is applied to one area. If a patient lies in one position for too long the skin on areas such as the bottom, heels, elbows, hips and shoulder blades becomes red and then begins to wear away. Disabled people loose the feeling in their paralysed limbs and body and therefore will not be aware that this 'erosion' is happening. The process does not stop itself, and so without treatment the sores just grow in width and depth.

A striker bed is designed so that a mattress can be screwed on top of the person, making them become the filling of the sandwich. The bed then pivots in its frame through 180 degrees so that the person is now facing the ceiling rather than the floor, and the neck has not been moved at all so the unstable fracture has been kept still through out the procedure. The old bottom mattress is now taken away and the patient left to admire the corrugated iron roof for the next two hours. It is easy to see how patients in this critical stage can become very depressed and dwell on their new position in life. They know that they will never be able to walk again and not many people hold much hope of ever doing anything again. It is essential to keep these patients occupied so that they have less time to think. During the two hours that they have to face the floor there is little that anyone can do for them. Therefore it is doubly as important to give the men menial tasks to do when they are lying on their backs. Carrying out the tasks means that they have to use their arms and hands which also means that the muscles are working which helps to prevent them wasting away.

I spent my first afternoon sitting on a wooden stool that had been made in the workshop, by the bed of Mohammed with a pile of gauze squares on my lap. My job was to hand one at a time to my reluctant partner and watch him as he folded it in a certain way so that it looked like an envelope. When the pile of folded gauze mounted to a respectable height a nurse came along and took them away to the sterilising pot (which was only a steaming pot). Once sterilised, the pieces of gauze were used as dressings.

Mohammed grew tired extremely quickly, but sometimes it was not altogether clear whether it was genuine fatigue or mere laziness. I soon learnt that "tham" meant stop, but I did not let Mohammed get away so easily. After an hour I too was more than ready to stop, though I think Mohammed was quite pleased that I had made him continue when he saw his day's work and knew that he had achieved something worthwhile. Mohammed was able to spend the next few hours thinking that maybe his life would be worth living after all, even if it meant taking things one small step at a time.

Once a week a young woman arrives at the centre laden with a large roll of the finely woven white gauze which her husband, Rob, makes back in their village. Rob fell out of a fruit tree when collecting the fruit and broke his back. Whilst he was a patient at the centre Rob was taught how to weave on a small loom and now he makes his living by selling the gauze to the centre. In the occupational therapy centre other patients are asked to cut the roll into squares before the striker bed patients are set to work.

As I was packing away I heard the mad cries of "aste aste" and saw a happy-go-lucky man speeding down the ramp at high speed, only just missing someone else who was waiting for someone to push him up the ramp so that he could go to bed in one of the six male wards. I now knew two Bengali words: 'tham' was stop, and 'aste' meant slowly. I moved out of the way because it was time for two orderlies to turn Mohammed over.

Back in the office I asked Mohua to explain what all of the different staff did, as they all seemed to have set duties. Mohua set aside the complicated accounts that she was working on and started to count on her fingers. There are five Sisters, all of whom have completed the three year nurse training. I was told that they were easy to spot because they all wore white saris and head pieces. The centre also employs six ward orderlies or care assistants who look after the men and carry out all the tasks that are not directly medical, which included the lifting of the patients. And there are a further seven male cleaners who keep all of the communal areas and male wards clean. The female patients are looked after by Ayahs who do both the jobs of the cleaners and orderlies but exclusively for the females.

Men and women are segregated in their social contacts through-out most of the Indian subcontinent and have been for centuries. This concept stems from the social order which dictates that women have no part in a man's social life. Physical contact is acceptable between members of the same sex but is considered very immoral between members of the opposite sex, and is considered to be almost on a par with an illegal sexual relationship. Although in the hospital situation the rules are considerably relaxed, some patients do feel uncomfortable being treated by a member of the opposite sex.

The centre also employs two occupational therapy assistants, one of whom is confined to a wheelchair and the other walks with crutches. There is a carpenter who has an assistant and three people who are employed in the metal workshop. The centre has a counsellor who also teaches written Bengali and maths to any illiterate patients. There are no resident Doctors at the centre but a few used to come in voluntarily each week for a few hours and were usually available if needed in emergencies. So all in all there are fifty members of staff who work for Valerie Taylor in looking after roughly sixty patients. The actual running of the centre is undertaken by the team of senior staff (one from each department) who take all of the decisions with Valerie as their mentor.

With only a days experience to reflect upon, I was struck by the incredibly positive approach towards everything in the centre by both the staff and patients.

Chapter 4

Basketball On Wheels

On the morning of my second day I stood outside the VSO guest house with Jackie, who I was sharing a room with. Jackie is a teacher for children with special needs and had been sponsored by VSO to work in the Protobondi school where Poppy was a pupil. She had already been in Dhaka for three months, so she knew the ropes. She had offered to assist me in finding a rickshaw to take me to work without being ripped off. As in many countries there is the Bengali price for everything and also the tourist price, which is usually about double. We stopped four rickshaws and tried to barter a price with them, but each time Jackie was not satisfied. Being early days I wondered why she was getting so worked up about the equivalent of eight pence, but Jackie pointed out that it is the principle of the thing.

Jackie had just agreed on a price with the fifth boy and trying to be helpful I held up ten fingers indicating ten Taka. The boy's eyes lit up with greed which puzzled me as only seconds previously he had been begrudging the agreed price. Unknown to me, I had actually just indicated forty Taka to the boy because each finger represents five and the thumb is ignored. Bengali's use their thumb to count each joint, the tip and then the nail on each finger starting with the little one. Finally, having sorted out the muddle and confirmed the original cost, I jumped onto the seat at the back of the glorified bicycle and waved goodbye to Jackie who cheerfully called out Good Luck.

Once on the move I wished that she had not called out her departing message because I suddenly became aware of what I was doing. The seat, which is a plastic covered wooden plank, gently sloped downwards and as the foot rest was only about two centimetres wide I had to clench my buttocks and hope I wouldn't fall. By the end of the ten minute journey my calf muscles were aching from the constant tension. But despite the discomfort of being an amateur I actually enjoyed my first ride on a rickshaw because the pace was so much slower than that of the motorbike, so I was able to see and absorb more of the general atmosphere.

I felt guilty at times sitting there whilst the thin and greying man sweated and puffed as he pedalled hard enough to make us move. His legs were very thin and all of the veins were standing out. When I thought that this man had probably spent the night sleeping under a piece of sacking on some pavement and only eaten a fistful of grain, it was a wonder that we moved at all.

The tiny bicycle bell did not bring me much comfort when we arrived at major junctions. People crossed regardless of the colour of the traffic lights, and all of the different types of vehicles moved when they felt like it. There is always a great deal of hooting and shouting at any Bangladeshi crossroads, and this one was particularly bad. A bus passed us so closely that the people hanging onto the outside knocked our rickshaw. We cursed them and they cursed us, all of which of course got us nowhere. The thought that I had missed the rush hour was daunting, but then the Dhaka roads look as though they are in a continual jam.

When we arrived at the centre the man tried to charge me 20 Taka, but I was not so easily fooled and gave him my 10 Taka note before hurriedly moving away into the safety of the centre. I had been advised to always try to carry the correct change, otherwise I might end up giving too much and not getting anything back.

Sport plays a very important role in the rehabilitation of most of the patients and normally takes place in the afternoons. Extra basketball practices had been scheduled for the next two days in preparation for the big match on Saturday, which seemed to be occupying everyone's every waking moment.

I did not get a chance to enquire as to why the match was so important because Swarup stopped me in the drive and asked if I would help transport some people over to the court in the Christian school across the road. I obeyed my orders and was directed to a man waiting by the gate in a newly painted blue wheelchair. I had been so preoccupied by my achievement with the trip into the centre that I had not noticed the group of twelve patients gathered at the gate. All of the wheelchairs had been freshly painted in either blue or green and all of the men and Mohua, the only female player, wore green or blue vests according to their team colour.

I was introduced to Chairman who had been at the centre for a couple of months and had earnt his name from being the chairman of a union of twenty thousand in his village. In October 1989 Julifkar Ali experienced a sudden onset of weakness in both lower limbs, he had developed Transverse Myelitis like Mohua. In our brief introduction I learnt that Chairman had a two year old daughter and a lovely wife who he could not wait to rejoin. So with me pushing we set off into the big city. I had found driving along the quiet country lanes in Hampshire hard enough (to the extent that I failed my test) but in comparison to what we had to go through to get to the court the experience paled into insignificance. We had to walk (or be pushed) along the road because the pavement was set about a foot above the road level and it was too difficult to get the chairs up the step. I pushed Chairman along the road going against the flow of traffic on one of the biggest roads in Dhaka. I kept on checking that I was doing the same as everyone else, worried that I was putting us both in danger of being squashed. We then had to get to the other side of this four lane road with at least six lanes of cars roaring down it. I just crossed my fingers and hoped for the best as Chairman shouted 'Go Sister' (the name given to all volunteers by the patients). The easy part of the journey over, I had to navigate our way through the bus and rickshaw station which is cleverly situated on a roundabout.

Wheelchairs are not the easiest things to steer at the best of times, and if you have ever tried to push a shopping trolley around Sainsbury's on a Friday evening you will be able to sympathise. But trying to get around moving people, impatient buses and through impossibly narrow spaces was hell. Once on the other side of the commotion I wanted to give myself a pat on the back but Chairman just chuckled and said that next time I would be less polite and therefore more effective.

By now I was sweating like a pig from the effort of pushing the heavy weight in the heat, but my attention was grabbed by a very funny sight. One of the patients had taken hold of the axle of a rickshaw and was catching a lift, unknown to the struggling boy pedalling. The member of the blue team was not as crafty as the green team for he was soon discovered and told in no polite terms to let go. The member of the green team had got onto a very good thing - he was holding onto a flapping strap hanging off the back of a babytaxi. These are motorbikes with an extension on the back and carry two people comfortably or as many as can fit uncomfortably. The driver of the babytaxi never cottoned on to what was happening despite the crowds that were staring in disbelief and laughing.

When everybody had arrived at the basketball court the game got under way. I was amazed at the standard of the play and the energy that the patients could find when they wanted to. Basketball is a firm favourite with the players and they will happily play for three hours twice a week. Watching Forrid refereeing I noticed that some of the rules were different, and that there is a limit as to how many turns of the wheel are allowed when in possession of the ball.

Swarup came up to me at the side line and introduced himself as the brother of Mohua. He is actually a student at the Dhaka university but spends a great deal of time at the centre both looking after his sister and helping out with the sport and many other activities in the centre. The government had decided to postpone all final exams so Swarup was in the horrible position of waiting. He had begun to explain about the big match when there was a cry from the court. Someone had tipped out of their chair and was sprawled on the ground unable to do anything. I was terrified and stood rooted to the spot dumbfounded. Swarup raced over to the man and hauled him back into his chair and the game went on as though nothing had happened. A few minutes later the same thing happened again, but this time everyone sat there in hysterics as they watched me run to the rescue only to find myself collapsing under the weight of the man and both of us ending up as a heap on the ground.

Swarup eventually found the chance to explain why everyone was so excited and why all of the chairs had been given a new coat of paint. On Saturday the two teams were going to play each other in front of the president's wife, Begum Raushan Ershad. The First Lady had visited the centre on a previous occasion and had been impressed enough by what she saw to want to help Valerie in the continuation of her work. At this time the future of the centre was in uncertain hands because, as I have already mentioned, the landlord was planning to turn it out of its home in Farmgate, and as yet there was nowhere else to go. Valerie had been trying to buy a piece of land in the country but had come across endless difficulties, making the purchase seem impossible.

The centre was putting on a match in the First Lady's honour in the hope that she would be able to provide some assistance with the buying of the land. The two basketball teams are the only teams in any sport formed by the disabled in Bangladesh, and Valerie hoped that it would help to encourage sport for the disabled across the country. Having said that, Saleh Ahmed, who is an occupational therapy assistant, went to the first International Disabled Games held in Nottingham in 1986 and won silver medals in both the shotput and javelin. Saleh Ahmed fell from a fruit tree in his youth and now walks with the aid of crutches.

The basketball game took place with an audience of fifty spectators, including the First Lady and the British High Commissioner, and under the curious eye of a television camera and many newspaper reporters. It was a wonderful game, enjoyed by all, but most of all by the players who had worked so hard.

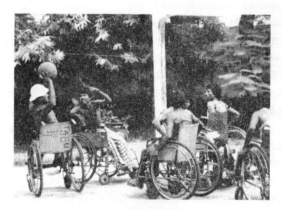

Basketball

Volleyball and badminton are now also played on the front lawn. Shotput, discus and javelin are thrown, and in the summer some patients are taken to a pond for swimming, using inner tubes for rubber rings. All sports help to strengthen muscles and help the blood circulation by making the body move. Balance is also improved, and the experience is fun for the players, though this last point might be debated by the females who are always reluctant to join in with any of the sports. I feel that it also helps the individual to be part of a team and to have to work with others and thus think about other people as well as themselves. It is so easy to become very self-centred during difficult times.

At three o'clock after everyone had finished their two hour siesta through the hottest part of the day, Farid and I, along with anyone else who was free at the time, had the daunting task of rounding up enough players to get a game of some sort going. There were always a few familiar faces of men who turned up each afternoon and seemed to enjoy themselves, but working up any enthusiasm in the others could be hard work. Farid used the tactic of just pushing an unwilling patient over to the net that had been set up, but I liked to try the gentler approach of verbal persuasion. Somehow we usually managed to muster up a large number of people, and would often have to play eight aside badminton. Inevitably at least one shuttle-cock or volleyball ended up in the empty concrete pond which meant that I had to jump in after it. Getting in was fine; getting out again was something else.

The teams were made up of strong basketball players and others who knew the rules, as well as weak patients who often had to play from a lying position. The sport sessions could become frightening when shotputs were being hurled in all directions, but it was always enjoyable being outside and once the patients were busy they too usually enjoyed themselves.

The best games were when the able-bodied people also got into wheelchairs to play. We were then consistently shown up by the patients! It is not until you put yourself in their position that you realise quite what a fight they are up against. Yet they fight with enthusiasm.

One day I found a swing ball set and put it up. I found a willing partner to play with me and gallantly offered to play backhand - to give him a chance I thought. When he thrashed me playing forehand and again when playing backhand I thought I would get my revenge by playing standing up rather than from a chair. If only!

In the evenings before the staff went home, two table tennis games were set up on the drive. One table was set at the usual height but the other one only stood at a foot above ground level so that the patients in low level trolleys could also play. Some patients opt to have a low trolley because it means that they are still at the same level as those who are squatting, which is a popular position for Bengalis to socialise and eat from.

But my time in Dhaka was not all taken up by playing games. There was a new language to be learnt, products to be made, and stomach-churning scenes to witness.

Chapter 5

Apni Bangla bolte paren?

(Do you speak Bengali?)

I had been in Bangladesh for a week, and was beginning to worry about where I could live: the VSO guest house was only meant to be a temporary measure. Two English volunteers had been renting a room in Gulshan, the smart district where all of the embassies are located. I went along to look at it, but did not feel happy about living there alone once Rob and Karen had left. The rooms were large and bare, and the facilities were unimpressive for the price the landlady was charging.

Another volunteer, John Wilkins, a man in his late sixties, was due to leave the next week at the end of his fourth visit. He suggested that I went back to his house to meet the Canadian family with whom he had been living, and after a cup of tea with Edward and Rosemary I was offered a room free of charge. Edward was working for CIDA, a Canadian agricultural aid project, and Rose-mary taught in the American school. They said that by putting me up for two and a half months they felt they were doing their bit to help the centre, which they certainly were and for which I was very grateful.

I moved into my own beautiful room. It had an ensuite bathroom with hot water, which was something of a treat after nine days of cold showers. Valerie was also pleased because housing her volunteers was causing difficulties at the time.

Holly joined me a few weeks later in the Charles' other spare room. Holly had come out for six weeks from Cheltenham where she works as an osteopath in a joint practice. At the age of twenty-seven she decided that she wanted to try something different, and had heard about Valerie through someone she had met at a party.

When Wendy arrived she was able to stay with a family who she knew from a previous visit. Having been a trader for Traidcraft for years, In 1988 Wendy went on a tour of India and Bangladesh to learn about the crafts that she sold in the antique shop she ran with her husband in Devon. Having heard about the centre from her neighbour, John Wilkins, Wendy decided to stay on in Dhaka for six weeks to help in the centre, and now returned because, like most other volunteers, she had caught the 'centre bug' and wanted to experience more, even if it meant leaving her husband and daughter behind for two months.

Every other day Khokon went to the post office to collect all of the mail: it was always exciting trying to be the first one to get hold of the sacred letter bag. One day I was out when Khokon arrived, so I called on Valerie when I returned to ask if I had any letters. She told me I had two, but that I would only be allowed them if I asked in Bengali. I suddenly realised that I had been in Dhaka for a fortnight and could still only say stop, slow and hello in the native language. I rushed around asking people the word for letter, learnt that it was 'chithi', and was rewarded with two of them. It is funny how bank statements follow you around the world!

I went to Madhab, the centre's tetraplegic counsellor, and asked for some Bengali lessons; I had had enough of sign language. We started straight away. I wrote down ten useful phrases and had to read them out loud until my pronunciation was passable. It was like being back at school as I was told to go home and learn them for my next lesson. I struggled through three lessons and about five phrases such as 'Apnar nam ki? Amar naim Corinna' ('What is your name? My name is Corinna') before it was mutually decided that maybe sign language was the answer after all. I remember being told something similar by my French teacher at school.

But my lessons were not over. Upstairs there are three male wards with about fifteen bored men in them. These patients are at their initial stages of their rehabilitation and have to stay in bed, and consequently they are often bored. Despite their timetable of occupational therapy and physiotherapy, they often seemed left-out and forgotten, except by one faithful person - Wendy. Wendy had brought a game of Connect Four from England and this became a life saver for the group of men in ward one. Whilst they played, Wendy always tried to hold conversations in Bengali, for which the patients loved her. They all had a great time struggling through with the help of a sacred yellow book called, 'Spoken Bengali: the common sense method', a book which became the volunteers' bible.

I found Wendy playing the match point with Khokon Nural Islam and told her about my failings with Madhab. She took me by the hand and marched me off to a bookshop where I purchased my own phrase book. I was sure I had the common sense required by the title, and felt determined to prove to Madhab that I was above sign language. Returning to ward one I spent an hour trying to chat with the men, who were highly amused by the long pauses between each word as I flicked through the pages trying to find the next part of a phrase.

Though it was slow-going at first, my progress was more impressive than with the school desk method, and I found it more enjoyable. Often the whole ward was in stitches listening to my attempts. If I gave up and pointed to the phrase I couldn't say I was met by blank faces of men who could not read Roman script. But the pointing decreased as my confidence and knowledge of their language increased.

Before embarrassing myself again with the inhabitants of ward one I joined two older patients who were sitting in the sunny back yard patiently knotting endless lengths of fine rope to make into fishing nets, for which there was a ready market in the city. Several false starts later I managed to explain to them that I wanted to learn their language, and was pleased when they clapped their hands in delight. However, it wasn't until later that I discovered how warped these lessons were. I cottoned onto their game just in time to prevent myself from getting into very silly conversations and from making doubtlessly rude comments. I decided that my faithful teachers upstairs were the only ones that could turn me into a bilingual genius. While I never reached that stage I appreciate that it was Khokon's patient help that enabled me to make small talk and ask for things in the market, direct people, and instruct my patients on how to do their exercises.

During my chats with Khokon and from talking to Wendy I found out that Khokon was one of Valerie's first patients. In 1974, aged seventeen, he fell from a palm tree and became completely paralysed in the lower half of his body. He had been a good student and after leaving the centre was set up in a shop selling oil, matches, biscuits, tea and sweets. But in December 1989 Khokon had to be re-admitted needing thirteen pints of blood on first arrival due to serious pressure sores requiring a hip operation. By the time Wendy and I got to know him he was on the routine of bedrest treatment for bedsores and occupational therapy. He told Wendy that he wanted to improve his English with her help and would in turn teach her Bengali - all whilst playing Connect Four.

Wendy once stopped me on the staircase as I was on my way to play a game of Connect Four. She said,

"I reckon he must be a good chess player because I swear he always plans three moves ahead of me, while reducing my concentration with that sexy twinkly-eyed smile of his." This photograph was taken by Wendy and made Khokon very proud. Wendy gave me the negative and parted with it, saying "it makes him so strong and handsome, and looking at him one forgets the withered body below his waist: the stiff hip, legs like matchsticks, and foot drop."

Khokon

Chapter 6

Second Week Blues

In the latter part of my second week I developed the Second Week Blues. I felt awful because I still felt depressed even though I had just moved into my luxury room and everyone went out of their way to be kind.

Until then I had been spending my time doing practical exercises with the three patients in the striker beds and with the men upstairs. Robbie had asked me to help Mohammed and his two companions in the corridor, to fold a newsletter and put it into an envelope which they also had to stamp. I knew it was important and that my participation was useful but I couldn't help thinking that three months of folding gauze and paper would be too much. The newsletters were sent to all ex-patients so that they could keep in touch with the goings-on of the centre.

Another task in which I became involved was the manufacture of paper bags upstairs with the patients of wards one and two.

Robbie packed me off with a bundle of old magazines and newspapers and several pots of glue, but gave me no instructions as to what to do with them. I was just told to try to generate some enthusiasm.

I need not have worried as I was welcomed by groans of despair: everyone knew exactly what the newspapers were for, and now I knew why Robbie had chuckled when he stressed the word enthusiasm. Not one to be defeated I decided upon some bartering. I said that the radio could be turned on as we worked, and this did the trick. One of the rules of the centre said that no music was to be played during the timetabled periods of the day. This was between nine and twelve in the morning, and between three and six in the afternoon. During these times everyone was supposed to be involved in some kind of treatment, and music was kept for the evenings. We set up an effective production line with three beds folding the paper and three beds gluing. I was the conveyor belt who carried the goods at their various stages to the next step. I think

Robbie was pleasantly impressed when I reappeared with roughly fifty bags.

The idea of these recycled bags was purely to bring in more money. Amazingly, a couple of hours work brought several Taka back into the centre because the bags were sold in the market to people who then filled the cone shape with nuts and set up stall on the streets. Nothing is ever allowed to be thrown away in the centre: the overflowing shed is sufficient evidence of that.

You have to be brave and strong to enter the shed because as soon as the door is opened you are in danger of being smothered by boxes of what looks like junk. It is, in fact, junk; but junk sells. All jars and old medicine pots are sold empty, pieces of cloth are remade into clothes or bedding for the patients, and any spare parts of machinery can either be sold or used again in the metal workshop. It makes our recycling attempts in Europe seem pathetic.

By the end of that afternoon I had learnt the tune of the number one song, which was obviously everyone's favourite. I had almost learnt the words to the chorus too, and I knew enough to join in when the ward broke into song. By the end of the day I knew the song was called Howa Howa and I too grew to love it, though partly because I had to if I was to stay sane.

Despite the warmth I received from both patients and staff I didn't really feel great for another week. Home felt distant in both space and time, but my spirits rose when Valerie told me that a British nurse was arriving. Theresa turned out to be a life-saver for me. She had been to the centre before as a young, unqualified volunteer with aspirations of a career in nursing. Now qualified, she was back for two years to train the medical staff.

When I explained how I often felt useless and that there was not enough to do it was Theresa who diagnosed the famous Second Week Blues. It was comforting to hear that she had experienced it too: the first week just whirls by and then in the second week you feel settled but lost. Theresa could have been my analyst with accurate perceptions like that, and she helped me further by writing a list of the sort of things in which she had become involved four years ago and then suggested that as I had studied Design and knew more about wood than anything else, I should visit the carpenters.

I knew how to sand wood and paint, even if at the end of the day

I looked like the painted object. I was told that encouraging the patients to participate meant that not only were they improving physically, but they were also improving psychologically. By using their concentration they had less time to ponder on their situation and future, and had the satisfaction of completing a project. It made them feel they were still worthy of living. Even the most hopeless cases were given a reason to live and a chance to regain their self respect (which is so often lost through disability) by Madhab who worked with each individual patient giving them counselling and general advice throughout their stay.

Feeling much better I went to visit the occupational therapy department where I found a hive of activity. Three patients were sitting in their wheelchairs, parked at the workbench sanding pieces of wood until they all slotted into place to make a jig-saw puzzle. All were content with their work and were deep in conversation. In the sewing room Jobeda was cutting out squares of plastic cloth as Jasmin held it. It made a gorgeous sight because Jobeda sat on a low-level trolley and Jasmin, who was only six years old, stood in front of her leaning against the table to keep her balance.

Jasmin wore a back brace made in the metal workshop and had learnt to walk again after her back was broken by friends sitting on her whilst playing. A nurse had discovered nits in Jasmin's hair and had treated it the only way she knew how, which was to shave her head. Poor Jasmin had been devastated to lose her long hair only weeks after her accident and became very depressed, cutting herself off from everyone around her. Thankfully she made fast progress and was walking with a frame within a month, and her good nature returned with her movement. Jobeda and Jasmin were laughing so much when I went in that I thought it best to leave them to it.

Gradually I moved further down the workbench and further away from daylight. At the end of the corridor, past the sewing room and painting room, Shemoll sat or lay for long hours at the lathe, cutting out the shapes to be made into crafts. Shemoll had been a carpenter before his accident when he fell from the third floor of a building and broke his back. An ex-patient and now a valued member of staff, Shemoll is the master key behind all of the wooden products produced for sale and for use in the centre. Everything from the bedside tables to the bookshelves are made in the centre's workshop. Shemoll can sit up in a wheelchair and often does, but chooses to do most of his work from a prone position because he is then less likely to develop pressure sores from sitting for long periods of time. For his hard work Shemoll earns 1800 Taka per month and has a small room in the centre.

Shemoll the carpenter at work

Shemoll and his assistant challenged me to use the hand lathe and cut out a koala bear puzzle. Two blades later I achieved it, much to the amazement of the men who had never before seen a female in the workshop. Few volunteers ever spend time in the woodwork area and consequently the carpenters seemed even more pleased that I could help out.

My next challenge was a race against Shemoll, so we sat side by side, shouted Go! and beavered our way around the template. All went well until I started to cut around the unfortunate koala's nose: I lost control and beheaded him, and therefore lost the race. Everyone was laughing and enjoying the new sport, so the next two templates became a course to be completed against the clock. This time it was a kangaroo, which was much easier to cut and enabled me to win by a few seconds. Shemoll and I were equals, and from then on if I didn't join him every day at the lathe I was in trouble.

I had bounced back to my usual enthusiastic and merry self and realised that there was more than enough to do provided I initiated the work rather than waiting to be told. New eyes often see things that other people pass over: with my light responsibilities I could dream up new ideas that permanent staff would be too busy to think of. When all these ideas began to pop into my mind I no longer objected to making bags with all the bedridden people, in fact I enjoyed it more knowing there were other things to be done as well. I even became a human bookstand for one man who wanted to read a newspaper but did not have the strength to hold it up. As I sat there I wondered whether I should own up to having designed a page turner but realised that it would not be a practical design in my new surroundings. The idea of a piece of machinery that could be controlled by the movement of a human eye was quite absurd now that I was in a country where a wheelchair is considered a luxury.

Everything was looking up and I realised to my considerable relief that I no longer noticed the smell in the centre.

I never really became involved with the metal workshop, but I know that Glen and company were always very busy. When a patient was admitted they would be assessed by the social worker and physiotherapist to determine the most appropriate type of walking aid for them. The metal workshop churned out tailor made walking frames, sticks, callipers, back braces and splints. Wheelchairs were for those who could not walk at all.

The wheelchairs tended to be one of two designs: either a normal wheelchair or a special low-level trolley. Many females opted for the latter because their future lives would most probably revolve around cooking, socialising, and sewing, all of which are carried out by able-bodied people in the squatting position or seated on the floor. It is often hard for the patients to return to their homes and be accepted back by their families and friends because so little is known about paralysis. Thus the fewer differences there are the better, and height plays a vital role in communication, so unless the individual's work prevents it, trolleys are recommended.

The wheelchairs are made from old bicycle parts and tubing bought in the local market. They are bulky and heavy but the patients preferred them to the western style wheelchairs because they felt safer, especially when they played violent games like basketball. There were very few imported wheelchairs in spite of many and frequent generous offers of donations because they usually turned out to bring more trouble than benefit. Once a foreign wheelchair had gone wrong it was usually impossible to find the parts with which to mend it, and even if it could be mended the cost was astronomical. Five wheelchairs were donated to Bangladesh during the 1991 cyclone, but were not discovered until five months later when they were useless. The chairs had been stored in a flooded room and it was estimated that to replace one wheel would cost £70.

The chairs produced at the centre are sold to outsiders at a cost of £100, which is the equivalent of an average year's salary in Bangladesh. Patients are asked to pay for as much of their wheelchair as they can realistically afford. For a few that means the entire amount, though most patients would only be expected to donate a minimal sum. At first this seemed mean to me, but it is easy to forget that Valerie depends on charity and that money does not flow freely into her hands when needed. Also, as Valerie explained, if people have to pay for their chair they are more likely to respect its value, to care for it and keep it in a working state. The same rule applies to walking frames and sticks. Some patients tended to take all of their free treatment for granted and expected everything to be handed to them on a plate, but the cost of one wheelchair means a great deal to the centre, so obviously the more patients who can pay the better.

Good news has arrived regarding the cost and design of the wheelchairs. David Constantine and Simon Gue won an award from the Royal College of Art for designing a wheelchair that can be made in the developing world using locally available material. They came to the centre and built a prototype of their design, at a cost of only £50, which proved very popular with the consumers, producers, and the accountants. In February 1991 the Motivation Team (David, Simon and another friend Richard Frost) returned to develop a self-financing workshop which will be able to produce the wheelchairs with no external support. They trained two members of the staff at the centre to produce the new design which is fully adjustable to suit each user, comes in three different sizes and can be folding or non folding. The team asked the patients what colour they would like the chairs to be painted in - yellow was the favourite because it symbolises warmth, happiness and hope.

The new workshop now produces twenty to twenty five wheelchairs a week and sells them to anyone who is interested as well as providing each in-patient with one. The Motivation team are a dedicated charity who are going on to design chairs in other third world countries. When they were at the centre they also educated the staff on how to position each patient in the chair to promote good posture and prevent pressure sores. The staff are now in a position to teach the patients about self care. David was able to boost everyone's moral because he too is a tetraplegic. The patients were amazed to see him organising and partaking in the setting up of the new workshop and could see the possibilities that are still available for themselves.

It was Simon's job to set the workshop up in the first place and to equip it with the necessary tools. He had already seen the average Bengali workshop from the first visit and knew that the tool boxes consisted of one screwdriver that doubled up into anything else that was needed. Simon also mentioned the mysterious half empty can of condensed milk that appeared on every work bench. Consequently the team had come well prepared and stocked up the centre's workshop with an array of shiny tools of all varieties. There was no shiny new metal to be found anywhere in Dhaka. One shop owner said to Simon,

"But Sir, we only have old bicycle parts and bits of old boilers. Will they do?" They had to.

As in the carpentry area, the patients help to make the metal products. It is not as popular as the woodwork because progress is slower and therefore less immediately rewarding. The patients are given pieces of metal to file down or something to paint and most of them stand as they work.

There is a workbench with straps attached to it at regular intervals. These are used to strap a patient to the table in a standing position in which they can balance, supported around the waist while they work on a piece of metal. This allows the leg muscles to strengthen from being used again, and improves the blood circulation from the sluggishness that results from long periods of non-use and the general immobility of sitting in a wheelchair.

Standing up again after such a long time can be a weird sensation, so standing practice is essential before a person moves onto the parallel bars. In fact it is impossible to expect anyone who has been on bed rest for months to sit up for any length of time let alone to stand. You probably know the queasy and spinning feeling you experience if you get out of bed too fast in the morning, well for a patient in the centre it would be a similar sensation, but a thousand times worse.

To help the transition from bed to chair a patient is strapped onto the tilting table. This is not a form of torture, but a way of allowing a person to gradually move from the horizontal to vertical position. The table can be fixed at different angles so before each session the table is tilted a little nearer towards the ultimate vertical position. The patient can grow accustomed to being upright again and avoid any shock. The vertical position for patients is best reached in as short a time as possible to try to prevent bed rest complications such as pressure sores, kidney failure, constipation and mental boredom. If a person has spent months lying in bed they cannot immediately sit up in a wheelchair because they will not have the necessary strength or balancing skills. The sudden fluctuation in blood pressure can cause a patient to faint. The tilting table is not a very popular piece of equipment with the patients, but it is an improvement from the old method of get up and if you faint, sit down and try again. As well as the balancing mechanisms being improved the leg bones are strengthened by weight bearing.

A major effect of long periods of bed rest can be Dropfoot. This occurs when the tendons in the foot contract, preventing it ever being lifted again, which means that walking is impossible. Many patients had toe clips like Shotorbabu's, though now the problem has been prevented due to a simple design by the Motorvation Team. A board is placed at a 90 degree angle to the mattress at the end of the bed so that the patient's feet rest against it and cannot drop forward.

Helping to make wood, cloth and metal products helps the patients to regain their confidence by proving that they are still capable of doing things, which in turn encourages them to think optimistically about the future. Some people learn new trades during their time at the centre and often find them more enjoyable than their old profession. Many of the male patients had their accidents in agricultural manual jobs. The centre strives to retrain every patient so that when they return home they can be self-sufficient and each person is given the chance to explore other skills they did not know; some men find that they have a talent for sewing or shop keeping. It is essential for them to be able to make money if they are to be accepted back into their homes. Females must re-learn how to cook and clean for their families.

One ex-patient that I met had been a struggling electrician before he fell off a roof and broke his back. He now owns three small shops and has much custom, the centre being a good source of income. Another man used to work in the fields for next to nothing and now has a prosperous tea shop in his village, bringing in enough money to support his wife and two boys.

Mohua is another grateful person who once said to me that if she had not suffered from Transverse Myelitis she would probably be a wife bound to her home and children in a small remote village. Transverse Myelitis is a dreadful disease which strikes randomly and mercilessly. Mohua was one of Valerie's first ten patients in the new six bedded centre and having made a good recovery was discharged back home in a wheelchair.

Valerie recalled the story to me from when she went to see Mohua on a home visit. Mohua was living in a flat several stories up, but was as determined as ever to get out and about. Going down the narrow spiral staircase was out of the question so the only way to get Mohua out in her fixed wheelchair was to lower them over the balcony using a rope pulley system. Valerie watched this incredible manoeuvre and knew that Mohua would go far and not allow her life to pass her by as she sat indoors helping her mother to prepare the vegetables. Valerie could not have been closer to the truth, but also could never have foreseen what an important role Mohua would lead for the centre and Bangladesh as a country.

As well as having been the centre's excellent secretary since 1984, Mohua travels extensively to attend conferences. She attended the conference that wound up the United Nations decade of work for the disabled. It was held in Finland and Mohua was very happy that two of her suggestions were included in the final meeting resolution. She is so dedicated to the CRP that she missed out on the opportunity of going to Sweden to see her brother so that she could be back in time to witness the laying of the foundation stone by the First Lady at the new site.

Mohua has also represented her country in Indonesia in a conference on community based treatment and in Nepal where a conference on self help for the disabled was held. Mohua gained a diploma in intermediate English geared to office staff from the British Council whilst I was at the centre. She believes very strongly that a lot has to be done to change people's ignorance towards disability and has made a large step in the right direction by starting up The Disabled Woman's Association in Bangladesh.

"At home I was very sick and lonely. I have learnt everything at the centre and it is my life. I am very happy here."

Mohua and Johuril

Chapter 7

Time Out

In Bangladesh the day of rest is Friday, when banks, offices and most shops will be closed. Friday was the day off for me and the other volunteers and senior staff, but it was a rather lonely day for the patients who were left with only a handful of essential staff between them - nurses, orderlies, and Ayahs. The afternoon treat was a video showing in the physiotherapy shelter for those who were able to wheel themselves out.

One thing I noticed was how proud the Bengalis are of their music and dance. In my last few weeks I went into the centre on a Friday to complete some work on a poster and was asked to sit down with the patients to watch a video of a famous singer and dancer. I explained to my neighbours that I could not understand anything, but they did not seem to think it mattered because I could hear the music and see the dance. I found a little went a long way and naively thought it very similar to Indian music.

On my second day off I ventured into New Market, which is the largest and liveliest in Dhaka. As forewarned a number of the stalls were shut, but this made shopping more pleasant as there were fewer people and more space in which to move. I had set out with very little money so that I wouldn't go mad on seeing the many tempting goods, but I was disappointed anyway. There were numerous stalls selling plastic buckets and containers alongside stalls laden with lengths of cloth to be made into saris. Most of the cloth was of a poor quality and covered with unpleasant-looking prints. I did find some food stalls which were wonderfully laden with heaps of different grains and spices and felt adventurous enough to buy a scoop of nutty things that people were eating like crisps. I never found out what they were but they tasted like burnt cardamom seeds - maybe that's what they were?

As I was about to give up and go home I spotted some ready-made shalwar kamises. Young women wear these before they marry, and then they move into saris. I found a couple in red and white striped cotton and held it up to myself as there was no where to try it on. The top was far too narrow and the legs too short. The owner of the stall spoke excellent English and explained that they were made for Bengali girls who do not have such large body frames as the English. He asked me to wait while he burrowed deep into a box and finally pulled out both a shalwar (baggy trousers) and a kamise (long straight top) that looked like they might fit. For a mere £2 it was a risk I was prepared to take.

I arrived at work the next day clad in my new outfit, feeling slightly conspicuous, but the new look was met with approval by all. I had made the effort to dress like a native, and this seemed to make me more acceptable to them. They thanked me for wearing their clothes, but I was happy in them anyway because they were comfortable to wear and practical to work in.

There was also great excitement in the centre one morning because a group of patients were going on an outing to the Dhaka zoo in the ambulance. Many of the patients come from remote villages and had never been to the city before, let alone seen anything like a zoo. Forrid, the social worker, chose the lucky eight patients to go and then we had the task of fitting the eight patients, eight wheelchairs and eight helpers into the ambulance.

We achieved the impossible in a reasonably short time. All patients sat on the two stretcher beds at the sides, while the middle was clustered with collapsed wheelchairs with volunteers perched precariously and uncomfortably between.

The ambulance, a Ford Transit, had been donated to the centre a few years before by the British High Commission in 1987 and had become one of the most precious and used items. Khokon drove the ambulance, though it usually required the help of some strong passers-by to get it started in the first place. Luckily it was not used as an emergency vehicle, so on the whole the effort and time involved in push-starting it caused no problems.

Unloading outside the zoo created much interest among the bystanders. The number of people and chairs that came out of one van would have amazed people anywhere in the world, but the very sight of any wheelchairs in Bangladesh is a rarity. Amongst the party were four British helpers, including myself, which also caused people to stare, even though Westerners are plentiful in Dhaka.

The procession of eight pairs set off together, but once inside the gates we decided to split up and reunite two hours later. I wisely chose Jasmin to push around; I say wisely because Jasmin was the youngest member of the centre and thus the lightest. Jasmin's is a sad story: she was playing in her village with friends who all sat on her back and literally broke it. She had been progressing very well and could walk around the centre with a backbrace on and using a walking frame which resembled a Zimmer frame. Touring the zoo would have been too much for her on foot, so for today's outing she was in a chair.

Jasmin loved the zoo, especially the Bengal tiger. Due to the combination of my blonde hair and the odd sight of a cared-for disabled child we found that the majority of people huddled around and pushing for a better view were in fact more interested in us than in the poor tiger. I felt quite claustrophobic, but did not mind until one particular man came up and said something in Bengali to Jasmin - something which obviously scared her. It transpired that the man had 'jokingly' threatened to throw her to the tiger. He then had the nerve to translate his sick little joke to me. Maybe because it was my first encounter with an unfriendly Bengali and because I was in unfamiliar territory that I too felt slightly threatened. But I need not have worried, because Forrid arrived and, standing at his full height of five feet, four inches, he told the man where to go.

After that experience Jasmin and I decided to stay with Forrid, and were also joined by Holly and her charge.

Having seen a terribly hot looking polar bear we found ourselves on a dead-end path. Instead of retracing our steps we voted for a short cut up a steep mud bank. I took a run up and arrived at the top panting. Jasmin, of course, was hardly out of breath. Looking back I saw Farid was making slow progress and Holly was well and truly stuck. Her patient was a big man and Holly was in hysterics trying not to let the chair roll back and squash her while she waited for help. I joined the struggle, but could make little impression on the problem. Only with Farid helping and Nuruzzaman turning the wheels with his hands did we manage to reach the top and join Jasmin and the others who had gathered to witness the fiasco.

Jasmin's eyes were streaming with tears from laughing so much and all she could do was complain that we had given her a stitch.

Vowing never to take short cuts again we waited for Theresa to return from buying everyone a cold drink before loading up the ambulance again.

Holly and I had optimistic plans of organising an outing for a handful of patients once a week so that everyone who was fit enough could have a chance to participate in the excursions. We made a list of the places we wanted to take them, which included such obvious choices as the beautiful mosques and old palaces, but also less likely places like the airport. The latter idea came about because so many patients expressed the wish to see an aeroplane when they heard us talking and complaining about our own flights. Sadly, for one reason or another, no more outings followed. I think everyone was too involved with the centre moving to Savaar at a moment's notice.

At the end of the afternoon I was ready to go home and collapse and waited outside the centre to hail a babytaxi. I normally travelled to and from work in one of these, partly because they were the fastest means of transport and also because rickshaws would not go so far. I was joined in my wait by an orderly, but he soon jumped into an overflowing Tempo. I just managed to ask him where the Tempo went before it cruised off into the distance. It was rush hour so there were very few empty babytaxis and the next thing available was another Tempo. I knew that it went to DIT 1, which was the bizarre name given to a big roundabout on my way home.

I climbed into the oversized babytaxi which was supposed to seat twelve but held at least sixteen people already. My fellow travellers were shocked to see a single female Badeshi (white foreigner) getting in and were annoyed that they all had to shuffle around to make room for me by the back and only door. I was already heading to the front where there had been a tiny space in the corner, but was pushed back again. I later learnt that there is always a set place for females to sit and in Tempos it happened to be by the door. This reduced the chances of physical contact, although a certain degree of contact was inevitable when the vehicle was so crowded.

Travelling by Tempo proved to be great fun. It has open sides with a tin roof which passengers thumped several times when they wanted to get off. At each stop the young boy who stood on a thin platform while holding onto the outside would quickly shout the destination. I thought they resembled the sound of the Australian wood pigeon. The journey cost only 2 Taka, and then I took a rickshaw the rest of the way home. Doing this regularly saved me 20 Taka each time.

I found travelling home late at night or after dark a little daunting, but not really more so than catching the tube in London at night. At least there were never any drunks to deal with since Bangladesh is a dry country, as dictated by the Muslim religion. People at the centre always tried to prevent me from going home alone late at night, but I had little choice as I could hardly arrive at a Bangladeshi's house with my nighty and toothbrush. At this time of night I was always sensible and took babytaxis rather than Tempos and tried to ensure that I never had to walk very far.

One evening the babytaxi I was in crashed into a car and instantly a fight developed between the drivers. Not wanting to hang around to witness the outcome, I just slipped away and found another babytaxi. Though I felt bad about not having paid the first man I had heard stories of guilty drivers being mobbed and killed in the street at the scene of the crash by sympathetic fellow babytaxi drivers. The golden rule, then, is to get the hell out of any crash area. The cause of our crash had been the severe lack of lights, though it was rare to find a vehicle of any kind with headlights that worked. In fact, rickshaws, Tempos and babytaxis do not even have them fitted.

On another occasion my pride got the better of me. I had just spent an evening with a few VSO's in the guesthouse and was determined to pay the correct price for getting home. Consequently I waited for three quarters of an hour and refused four rickshaws because they were asking too much. When the fifth one rolled along I made a snap decision to pay the asked amount as it had suddenly dawned on me how utterly ridiculous it was to be waiting in a dark and maybe dangerous street in order to save myself the equivalent of just six pence. I was cross, nonetheless, because earlier on that day I had shocked Swarup when he asked how much I had paid for my ride in a rickshaw. When I told him he gave me a disbelieving look and said that that was what he would pay. I felt like a true worker rather than a tourist, now that I was no longer paying tourist prices.

I felt mean not paying a little more to each driver knowing what poverty they lived in, especially the rickshaw boys, but I also believed that I was entitled to the right price as I was a worker myself and on a low budget. If the man was friendly or helpful I would tip him a little as I would in a black cab.

Chapter 8

The Masochist Marathon

Robbie was busy painting old powdered milk cans blue and then writing a message on them in both Bengali and English. The message read: 'Buy a brick for the centre'. With a slot cut in the lid the old cans now served as piggy banks. A special Muslim prayer called Milad was held in the yard to pray for the success of the future centre (to be built as a replacement after the eviction from the current site) and to start to fill the can. Each patient and staff member passed it around, adding their donation. Since then, every patient has been encouraged to contribute 3 Taka (about £0. 06), which Valerie hopes will make everyone involved feel like it is their centre and help to secure its future.

The centre has many friends in Bangladesh, all of whom help to contribute some of the cost of keeping it running, but the response to the plea for bricks astonished even the optimists. Having been an avid Blue Peter fan in my youth I knew all about money thermometers, so I drew one and hung it up on the wall in the office. Our goal was ten million Taka, and each time money was donated someone filled in the chart.

There is a club in Dhaka called the BAGHA (British Aid Guest House Association) where aid workers and diplomats can swim and sip back a gin and tonic or gulp back a cold beer. Members of BAGHA can also use the British High Commission Club, which has a bigger pool. I had been introduced to a very kind family in the High Commission through my father who made me a member of the two clubs. Not only was it very nice to be able to now and then escape the hustle and bustle of Dhaka, but my membership also became very useful.

One Friday, Holly and I spent our day off being thoroughly lazy by the pool, until we exerted ourselves to swim one hundred lengths in just under an hour. I have always enjoyed swimming but had never taken the sport seriously or swum any great distances until that Friday when I suddenly had the idea of doing a sponsored swim for the centre. I was convinced that unless I managed to swim for some ridiculous length of time no one would bother to sponsor me, so I hit upon six hours. I think it was the doubts in people's minds that made me even more determined to try it out, and then the generous response from people that stopped me chickening out.

Elizabeth, the eldest child of Rosemary and Edward Charles, listened to me whittling on about my mad idea, and enthusiastically asked to join in with the swim. I was touched that she should want to put herself through such agony, and pleased that there would be the chance of more publicity and more money.

Between us we collected £800 worth of sponsors, and it was the image of this figure in my mind that got me through the last hour. Elizabeth ended up swimming six hours at a different time to me so that between us we swam for twelve hours, from eight in the morning until eight at night. This meant we could not egg each other on with every stroke, but I did watch her from the poolside and gave moral support as she had no other spectators (it was a school day and her friends were slogging over their desks at the time). I tried to brighten up her six gruelling hours in the way that others were to do for me.

The Connellys, my friends from the High Commission, helped me raise much of the money by badgering everyone in the office. As everyone knows Valerie they were only too happy to oblige. Mike, here visiting his parents, paced me for a total of three hours. When he wasn't in the water he sat on the diving board reading out dreadful jokes from a book of a thousand jokes. Despite their lack of humour they did help to combat the boredom. During my five minute intervals each hour there were always a few spectators waiting with hot cups of tea and Smarties, which momentarily made me forget my aching limbs.

During the last hour it started to get dark, and then the rain began. But I was in the middle lane and egged on from either side by Mike and Bob, a visiting mechanic. I will never forget the relief I felt when someone from the side shouted that there was just one minute to go. We were at the deep end, by the steps, so I said I would do two more lengths and then finish. I somehow found the strength to crawl the last of seven hundred odd lengths (about seven miles) and was amused to stop and see a crowd of well-wishers. Or had they come just to check if I had done it before departing with their money?!

The next morning I gingerly walked into the office and was met by lots of staff, all congratulating me. I was only sad that Elizabeth, being at school, was not present to experience the electric atmosphere when Valerie opened my card and announced the amount of money we had raised. No one, least of all myself, was expecting it to be so much. Elizabeth was to receive her share of the heroine's limelight the following week when she came in.

Salam was leading the weekly meeting with all of the patients. I was led over to them holding the thermometer chart and a big red pen. Sponsored events are quite a novelty for most Bengalis, so Salam had to explain what I had done. I have to admit that I had never felt so good or proud as I coloured in a large chunk of my thermometer. Some never did grasp the concept of why anyone would want to swim for six hours or why anyone would pay you for doing so, but they did understand what 33, 255 Taka meant. The architect took out his calculator and worked out that I had just bought 11, 085 bricks - enough for a small building. The weekly meeting continued, enabling the patient's grievances and problems to be heard and providing the opportunity for the disabled members of staff and social workers to give advice to the patients about the daily running of the centre.

The local staff also put a huge amount of effort into producing a brilliant play, a tragic drama about love and death. Everyone was transformed from their hospital role into a very convincing new character as they acted them out in a small theatre. Luckily some kind soul had typed out an English precis. It was like going to the opera in that while it helped to know the general story, the quality and buzz of the performance were enough. It seemed that acting ability was one of the necessary staff qualifications for working at the centre!

Getting to the theatre was like a repeat performance of the trip to the zoo. This time the ambulance transported many more patients as well as props - the biggest of which was a live goat.

Money is not the only benefit to accrue from these events, for the publicity the centre gains is equally valuable. For this very reason I produced a small exhibition on display boards of life at the centre and how it would not be able to continue if it were not for the help it received. The boards were positioned in the foyer so that the audience had to walk past them on their way to their seats, and they conveniently passed a collection box on their way out. Friends back in England would have had a giggle if they had known I had been asked to do the posters - especially those with whom I shared Design class. Yet it was because I had mentioned that I had studied Design that I had landed myself a new role at the centre.

After such an enjoyable evening, Theresa, Holly and I thought it would be an anti-climax to go straight home, so we opted for a drink at the Sonargaon - the top hotel in Dhaka. But having emptied our pockets and purses previously we could only pool enough money for a coke each, so we made up on the free peanuts and ate the bar out of them.

Chapter 9

Hold My Hand

During Wendy's first visit she discovered the value of make-up and nail polish, for all of the female patients loved Wendy and her make-up bag, and the males were intrigued by her too. Past experience had taught Wendy to arrive with a bigger make-up bag and more bottles of perfume.

The centre only has one female ward with eight beds. At the time there were ten patients, so the children shared beds. There are several reasons for the distorted ratio between the sexes: the majority of the patients end up in the centre as a result of industrial and agricultural accidents, the most common being falls from fruit trees and buildings. There are also now increasing numbers of road accident cases, though the number is still amazingly low considering what I saw when travelling across the city several times a day. So by the very nature of the accidents more men fall victims since in a Muslim country the women stay at home to look after the house, children and crops.

The Muslim factor also means that females are not considered to be as important as men, and they are often left to die if they have a serious accident. Very few people realise that life can be worth living with a broken spine because so little is known about the available treatment for such cases.

Jobeda is a typical example of how women are mistreated. In January 1988 a mud wall collapsed on her and her three month old son. Thankfully her son escaped unhurt, but Jobeda was less lucky. The weight of the wall had broken her spine and left her paralysed at the age of only nineteen. Nobody in Jobeda's remote village knew what to do, so they just carried her into another hut where she stayed for three weeks until, by pure coincidence, professional help arrived.

When Brother Joseph found Jobeda, a large chunk of her spine was sticking out of her back, and she had no movement in her legs. By the time Brother Joseph had returned with Jobeda to Dhaka and admitted her to the centre, her spine had set in the new distorted position. Having assessed Jobeda's situation, Valerie reluctantly decided that straightening Jobeda's back and the long aftercare that would entail were beyond the limited resources currently available.

A low level trolley was made for Jobeda, on which she can now get around, and she has also learnt to walk a fair distance with a walking frame. She can now work a small weaving loom and earns her living selling her woven cloth to the centre - which brings in 150 Taka (£3) a month. I never saw Jobeda without a beautiful smile even though she was going through hell at the time trying to win a court case which would give her the right to bring up her own son, as she is entitled to do under Bangladeshi law.

Jobeda

Jobeda was re-admitted to the centre while the court case was going on. Her husband had abandoned her at the time of the accident and taken their son with him claiming she was no longer fit to be a mother.

She would remember that one day she ran,
She would remember that one day she had fun,
Would anyone bring to her the son?
(Extract from a poem by Husnara Kamal, entitled *Jobeda*).

One of my most memorable afternoons was when I saw the ambulance arrive back from the court hearing. Khokon would not say anything as he opened the doors and let the ramp down. First out was Valerie, and then I saw Jobeda being pushed down, backwards. When she turned her trolley round a beautiful boy was sitting on her lap, looking bemused.

Wendy was famed for her hand and foot massages. When not playing Connect Four she was paying personal attention to individual patients upstairs by massaging their hands and then painting the men's fingernails before squirting some perfume onto their wrists. Few full-time staff have time to sit and chat, so Wendy's undivided time was a treat for everyone. The movement promotes blood circulation, so her massages were of medical importance too.

During Wendy's last few weeks she encouraged me to start helping her on he 'hand and foot rounds'. At first I was hesitant, never having had such close physical contact with any of the patients before and I knew that there were high standards to live up to. My anxiety was not lessened when I went to my first patient to give him a foot massage. I thought a foot was the easiest thing to start on as the patients cannot feel them, but even then it was not straightforward: as I picked up my patient's foot a large clump of rotten skin fell off into my hand. I battled not to show my disgust and continued to clip his toe-nails, but the clippers broke because his nails were so thick. I then hurriedly moved on to his hands. Ashamed as I was of my pathetic behaviour, I never went near a foot again. I tried to make up for it by doing more hands, but I knew I was not cut out for the job.

Poppy often cried out, ''Hold my hand, mummy, '' because it helped to steady her spasms. I felt that everyone was calling out the same plea, ''Hold my hand'', purely for the comfort that the simple gesture could bring. It was also probably the same cry to come from the entire disabled population in Bangladesh, though many were not fortunate enough to be heard.

I became involved with another of Wendy's regular tasks in the centre. Mr Bimalendu was so very much Wendy's patient that I asked her to tell his story and how we both came to feed him his daily feast...

Mr Bimalendu was a patient upstairs in the small men's ward. A teacher of science, he had been admitted in February 1990 with paralysis in body and limbs. He had some feeling in his feet and hands, but no strength. One day he asked me if I'd feed him some fruit every morning - peel an orange or feed him grapes or a bite from a banana. Fresh fruit was an expensive luxury for most people, but he obviously knew it was good for him and a relative bought him a twice weekly supply.

Quite how his fruit feeding took on such manic importance I don't know. Days became planned around the twelve noon slot. Big starred messages were left all over the place if either Corinna or I couldn't be there - 'Don't forget Mr Bimalendu's fruit - 12 o' clock - & don't be late!' Perhaps it was the beseeching and disappointed, let-down look in his eyes that made me realise how important that small task of help was to him on the one day I forgot to turn up as planned. Regular timekeeping, seemingly of no importance whatsoever to the rest of Bangladesh's population, was vital to him. If I said midday that was when he expected me there, and in a typical schoolmaster/pupil fashion I did as I was told.

The ritual was always the same too. It didn't matter if I'd washed my hands seconds beforehand. He always intimated that I was to wash them again within his view at the tiny cold water sink out on the verandah. One had to remember to do things in the Muslim way, and the fruit was always offered with the right hand, not the left. But Mr Bimalendu was generous too. After every third segment of orange or grape he would say 'Do you eat?' and would get quite upset if I didn't share it with him and the other three patients in that room would always be offered a biscuit, if not fruit. ·

One night during the interval at the theatre (a play put on by ex-pats at the American School), Corinna and I found ourselves totally collapsed in giggles. Like two naughty schoolgirls we ached with uncontrollable laughter. I think it was all to do with making plans that had omitted fruit-feeding, sin of sins, though quite what set off our mirth heaven only knows. It was a moment we will never forget!

It may sound as if we were making fun of Mr Bimalendu, but this was not so. His paralysis was inexplicable and had devastated what had probably been the ordered and relatively well-off exist-ence of an educated man. The very best moment of my time in Bangladesh came on the last day of March, just days before returning to England. As I went to put an orange segment into his mouth he intimated not to do so. Instead, slowly, oh how very slowly, his hand moved towards my palm in which lay the fruit. Painstakingly he held the fruit in his fingers and then began the equally long journey back with it to his mouth. Everyone in that room watched silently, intently, willing him to succeed, and on doing so there were shouts of joy and congratulations and beaming faces all round.

So for the first time he fed himself that day, dropping only a few grapes to the floor. All of a sudden there was hope in his eyes. A hint of progress that at last made his recovery seem a possibility.

Mr Bimalendu was also perhaps an example of how a volunteer might help, by having the time to sit with patients and observe their needs, which overworked staff sometimes fail to do. It seemed wrong that this man was not enjoying reading as he lay flat all day, mostly on his stomach, his head just propped on a pillow. But where could he prop a book and how anyway to turn the pages? On making enquiries with Robby, the occupational therapist, I found out that there were reading frames lying covered with dust some-where in the bowels of the storeroom and he quickly saw to it that this patient had one. As for turning pages, although it was a very slow process, with the aid of a rubber thumb tool on his finger, Mr B could now manage it for himself. This was good physiotherapy practice plus, surely a great feeling of independence, of doing something for himself by himself.

A daily newspaper was brought in and he was able to read it to the others. It was asking for suitable books for patients that led Corinna to discover Madhab's library - an old wardrobe full of what, to our eyes, looked like ancient, tatty books, but which were nonetheless still readable. There was a lending library ticket system too, but badly in need of updating and Corinna spent days getting this in order, much to Madhab's approval.

Watching Mr Bimalendu turn the pages so effectively with his rubber thumb made me wonder if my A' Level design project had been necessary. It is as easy to forget about the differences between the two countries whilst in Bangladesh, as it is at home. My page turner had a market in Britain were there is money (although not nearly enough) to spend on luxury aids for the less fortunate, but in Bangladesh a person is lucky to have a wheelchair. It is unrealistic to try to compare Western Europe with South Asia for when I was doing my project Neil Slatter argued that a page turner was not a luxury item for a person confined to a wheelchair who, in general, has many lonely hours to fill in. Whereas if a disabled Bengali happened to be literate, I would think that a page turner would probably be the last thing on their priority list.

It was a month before Madhab's 'birthday'. He no longer celebrated his date of birth, having replaced it with the day of his accident because he believed that in recovering he became a better man. Madhab slipped off a roof when he was fourteen and was left tetraplegic (paralysed from the shoulders down), though he still has some movement in his arms. Anyway, Madhab asked me to go into old Dhaka to buy some more library cards to begin the updating of the small mobile library.

The address I had been given did not seem to exist. Wendy and I found the street and tried to explain to about a dozen shops and offices what we needed, but to no avail. Tired, hot, and on the verge of getting angry we voted to go home empty handed. It was on the way home that I wondered if it was really necessary to spend the estimated amount of about £60 on two hundred library cards when to make them would not be so difficult.

I found myself heading for a nearby stationery shop to buy some large sheets of card. Back at the centre my enthusiasm dropped when I realised the size of the job I had let myself in for. Then I badgered Chairman into helping me cut out the shape of the envelope that would eventually be stuck inside the front cover of each book to hold the slip with the borrower's name on. Swarup had spent a vast amount of time transferring all of the centre's millions of hand-written notes regarding patients, meetings and accounts onto a new mini-computer that had recently been donated to the centre. He was the only person who had the brains to work it and kindly offered to print out the instructions for each library card.

Several days later I purchased some glue and took my box full of card shapes up to wards one and two to try out my luck. The men were even less enthusiastic than they had been about the paper bags and at first they refused because they knew this wasn't an order from Robbie as part of their rehabilitation. It was only my charm that finally won them round, and we made a few every day whenever I had a spare hour. This was all kept quiet from Madhab, who thought that I had forgotten about it.

Madhab's 'birthday' was celebrated by most of the staff over supper at a friend's house. I presented my box of new, one hundred per cent home-made library cards, glad to be finally rid of them.

During Madhab's long convalescence he discovered that he had a talent for painting. A specially constructed handsplint that held a paintbrush was made for him, and the results have been incredible. He paints in water colour and enamels and works in amazing detail. To do so, he lies on his bed face down with a board extending from under the pillow on his right side. All of the movement that he uses comes from his right shoulder only.

He manages to capture the spirit of Bangladesh superbly, and many of his paintings are of images of flowers, rivers, birds and sunsets which are all indispensable parts of life in a fishing village where he grew up.

"...hit by the world's most tremendous cyclones and slaughtering storm waves, eternal floods, crushing tornadoes, cutting hailstorms; surrounded by deathful disease: still living on with music in their heart and flute in their hands."

-This quote about the people of Bangladesh (from Gerry Svedlund's book *Spoken Bengali*) highlights the sense of Bangladesh being a country of hope, in spite of the difficulties faced by its inhabitants. Madhab's paintings illustrate the same point with the characteristic harsh black exterior and glowing red interiors and his beautiful scenes of rural Bangladesh.

In May 1989 Madhab had his first exhibition in the British

Council where he showed twenty-five paintings under the title 'Views From The Heart'. Each painting was framed by the centre's own craftsmen, and fifteen of the twenty-five were sold. Since then they have all sold.

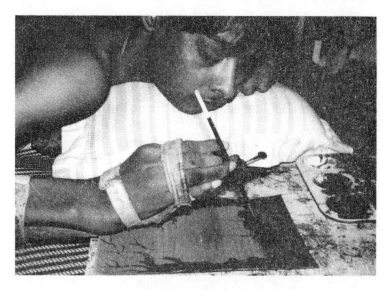

Madhab Painting

Chapter 10

Cooking Pot Commode

Two weeks into my time in Bangladesh Holly arrived. At the time I thought Holly would slip straight into the routine because she was trained in something useful. Holly was the first to admit that during her tour of the centre she wandered where she could fit in. Selfishly, her initial apprehensions helped me to realise that maybe I was not a freak who could not find a niche for myself as both Theresa and Wendy did instantly. It only then dawned on me that they had been to the centre before and knew what to expect to find.

I was delighted to see that it took Holly just a few days to find where she could fit in and then there was no stopping her, whether it was a week day, Friday, late at night or during the lunch hour Holly seemed to always be hard at work. With her knowledge of the overlap between physiotherapy and osteopathy she was able to contribute to the needs of the patients enormously. Holly also helped to lift me out of my gloom by including me in what she was doing and why. I was continuously learning and felt more able to participate in the many different activities going on around me.

When I sat down to write about the physiotherapy side of things in the centre I came across a blank and soon realised that I would never make a good job of it, so I rang Holly and put on my best pleading voice. I need not have bothered with the rehearsed voice because Holly was more than willing to write the next few paragraphs for me.

Osteopathy and physiotherapy are both concerned with the body frame work and how it is functioning. Our aims are to restore function and movement where possible and to encourage a better blood supply to the area. If these two aims are achieved the health and strength of vital tissues are improved which allow us to achieve our daily physical tasks. To a Bengali it is even more important to be physically fit as so much of their lives depend on being able to fend for themselves in the toughest conditions.

The differences between osteopathy and physiotherapy lie in the fact that osteopaths have no hospital training in Great Britain, they can only work in a private practice which means that the type of patient seen by each therapist is very different. Our patients are not as seriously physically incapacitated and will present varying degrees of pain.

We, of course, learn about the management of the paralysed patient, but the personal, first hand experience is minimal. With my knowledge and experience of the last eight years I realised that I would have to adapt my techniques and management programme to meet the needs of these very much more disable people. This is where the challenge lay for me.

By the end of my first week I was beginning to get an idea of how the department worked. The head male and female physios had recently returned from an international conference in India to further their skills which they could then pass on to the men who had been trained at the centre with varying years of experience. The sex of patient and therapist remained the same wherever possible. The women were happy for me to treat them and on the whole so were the men, apart from three or four who strongly objected.

On the first Thursday morning I attended the weekly ward round with all the other therapists, doctors, nurses, the social worker and counsellor. It is during this time that a representative from each department get together to work closely in conjunction with each other to aid each patient's rehabilitation to the full. This was my opportunity to learn about each patients history, their management programme to date and discuss the next step. I managed to get notes down with the hope of being able to do some study for each I was going to become involved with.

At first I became involved in working on the women's ward, each patient being treated very individually in relation to their capabilities. An outline of a treatment programme would be as follows; bed rest for six to eight weeks would be necessary if the injury was recent and the spine needed immobilising to promote healing, or secondly if pressure sores were present. Passive exercises would follow where the therapist moves the limbs for the patient and in doing so exercises as many joints as possible and stretches out shortened and contracted tissues as a result of disuse or high levels of spasticity respectively. Acute exercises (where the patient starts working his body alone) are gradually introduced and at a much earlier stage if the upper body is undamaged. All this work is encouraging the re-learning of body movements as well as tissue health and strength.

We all made use of the few aids that we had. For example, we played ball with patients in the back yard which helped their sitting balance. The patient may then be able to advance on to exercising their walking at the parallel bars with or without leg splints or even start on a walking frame. The majority of the patients worked hard for themselves and the team. They wanted desperately to get back to their homes and families; they put their all into it. Progress was frustratingly slow for them, but if they could just see that tiny improvement each day or each week it meant that there was hope. My broken Bengali created a few laughs, but I was actually understood which surprised me.

Another part of my week was to attend to the out patients clinic twice a week. The majority had suffered from strokes and because of the limited space and resources in the centre Valerie had to put a boundary on the people that she could accept as in-patients and came to the decision that stroke cases had a better chance of survival in a government hospital. Thus, they came on an out patient basis so that they could use the equipment and be taught new exercises to do at home. Tucked away in the corner was a home made, solid wood couch which I ended up treating most of the staff on who were suffering from pain in their lower back as a result from lifting patients improperly.

Having worked on many different patients by the end of the first month, it was decided that I would concentrate on just a handful, two of whom I particularly wish to mention.

The first was a warm, gentle, patient man named Shotorbabu who had been blind for several years and recently suffered a stroke. He had previously given singing lessons at the centre and because of that he was admitted to CRP. He had become quite depressed by his situation and constantly wondered whether he would ever be able to manage on his own again. I carried on with the treatment programme devised by a British physiotherapist who I had man-

aged to work with for a while. Shotorbabu was at the stage of walking at the parallel bars and what we really needed was a good pair of shoes, but we couldn't think where to get them from. As luck had it a friend of the centre had just donated a smart pair of black city lace-up shoes which were a perfect fit. The workshop then made a lower leg brace for him so that Shotorbabu was all set to go. Our goal was to see Shotorbabu walk again.

In the mornings I exercised all of Shotorbabu's joints and then supervised his exercises on the bed. In the afternoon we worked at the parallel bars and ended with a good walk. Our finishing post was the old Bangladeshi fruit seller who each day religiously parked himself about a quarter of a mile up the road from the centre's gate. He moved on fast and what a joy that was to see. We carried on with our routine, each day getting that little bit closer to where we wanted to be. The heat of the day obviously did not have the same draining effect on Shotorbabu as it did with us Westerners. After being exercised he decided to go on and do more on his own at the parallel bars. I was with another patient at the time when a nurse called me to go out into the yard, Shotorbabu wanted a word.

Shotorbabu had no words for me, what he wanted to show me was his first steps completely unaided. I was moved to tears and ran up to him in my excitement and showered him with praise. There was no looking back, I now felt sure he'd win his battle.

The other patient I wanted to mention was a young, newly married man who always welcomed me with brave warm smiles. His name was Fozzil, and his accident had been as a result of carrying a heavy load on his head, and was now paralysed from the lower neck down; a tragic sight. We worked hard together helping him to re-learn all the basic body movements which one learns so easily as a child. I have never seen such determination in a man who seemingly had so little to look forward to.

One of the first movements to work on was those necessary for feeding himself. It would be humiliating to have to be fed by someone else in front of others. Fozzil was finding it very difficult to use his right arm, the arm always used by Bangladeshi people for eating. The effort and energy necessary to raise his arm was so great that beads of sweat formed on his brow. He never gave up and

with his willpower there was a tiny step forward each day. I wasn't
sure how far we would get, but we always just looked ahead.
   It was now getting closer to when I was due to leave. I had made
sure that these patients would be followed up by Corinna who I
knew would put all that she had to give into the job. She had worked
with me over a period so I felt confident that she knew what to do.

I was touched that Holly had such faith in me and also nervous that
I should live up to her high expectations. It was a proud making
moment for me when I was given two of my own patients. I was still
an on-looker when Fozzil accomplished his first great feat which
was to eat a biscuit. At first Holly had set up a sling which was
suspended from the ceiling to support his arm as he physically
moved it from left to right and up and down.
   Everyone has to be resourceful at the centre to make up for the
lack of equipment. With a little imagination and initiative most
items have been covered. Car inner-tubes become cushions and
cooking pots commodes. The next stage was to dispose of the sling
and to replace it with my own hands. I then had more control on how
much support Fozzil was getting and could lessen the amount
slowly. I found the frustration and disappointment written across
Fozzil's face painful to look at during the beginning, but the
determination also came across.
   During the hours spent on doing these monotonous exercises I
tried to chat with Fozzil even though he knew no English. I gathered
that he was only eighteen years old and his wife fifteen. He had had
no form of education and was desperate because he had to bring in
money for his family and the only way he knew how was through
manual labour. In Holly's last few days Fozzil triumphantly ate his
biscuit without any help from us or the sling. He was doubly
pleased that Holly had been able to see him achieve the first goal
in his management that they had both worked so hard for. It was not
long until I had to take the biscuits away to prevent him from
growing fat!
   I was advised to replace the biscuit with an educational puzzle
which involved slotting different shapes into the correctly shaped
hole. It made Fozzil turn the shapes around, performing the
twisting motion in the wrist. It was a joy to watch the impressive

improvement in Fozzil's movement in his upper body but his legs were another story all together. Rhoman asked if I would be interested in helping him do Fozzil's passive exercises. It was good to see the whole of his treatment and to be introduced to the more specialised work of the physiotherapists.

In the evenings we set aside half an hour to work on his legs which were extremely spastic. We basically bent and stretched each joint in every working direction. It is amazing how strong one needs to be and on more than one occasion I was defeated, trying to straighten Fozzil's muscles which would involuntarily bend the other way or contract further making our task very tiring. Rhoman had little hope in the poor man ever walking again and I must say that it was not hard to understand why. I increased my rounds in the evening with Rhoman to five patients.

Both the family and patient are taught to carry out passive movements so that on discharge the exercises can be continued. The physiotherapists spend an average quarter of an hour with each patient every day in comparison to an estimated three hours in Stoke Mandeville. One physiotherapist at the centre does the job of several therapists in England.

For example, there are no speech therapists or trained occupational therapists who have special training in the movements of the hands. Robbie has obtained all of his knowledge from the centre, but his lack of formal training is compensated by his care and dedication. Robbie gives the patients everything he possibly can, but no amount of care and love for his job can make up for the finer details so desperately needed for each individual. With everything considered the work done by Hosneara and Rhaman is even more commendable.

A year later I shouted with joy on reading the fantastic news that Fozzil had just been discharged home, walking with a frame. I immediately rung Holly who at first could not believe the news bought by a letter from Theresa. When it finally sunk in I could sense the pride and joy in Holly's voice.

By the time I took on Shotorbabu he was already well on his way to recovery so all I really had to do was accompany him on his daily walks around the centre and out into the busy streets. Shotorbabu was in his element during these walks and never stopped talking.

My new words in Bengali such as up, down, left and right became very handy as Shotorbabu had the added difficulty of being blind, which makes balancing harder and obviously knowing where to go. One afternoon when we had reached the gate, Shotorbabu asked me to stand aside and watch what he had been secretly practising ever since Holly had shown him what to do. He handed me his walking stick and then slowly bent down on to his haunches and then stood again with complete control and never once swaying from side to side. I was dumb struck.

Normally the crowds of people who sat on the wall looking at the goings on of the centre annoyed me intently. I wanted to shoo them off and let the patients play their games or just enjoy the cool breeze without feeling as though they were part of an exhibition. I knew that my feelings were not shared by the Bengalis themselves who expect large crowds and gain security from them, but none the less I could not shake them off. Yet as I watched Shotorbabu walk away I wanted the whole world to see and to witness this symbolic sign of Shotorbabu walking back in to the world of independence.

Strokes usually leave their mark on the individual for the rest of their living days by causing the right hand side of the body to remain weaker than the left. Shotorbabu was no exception and it was visible when he walked for he dragged his right foot. The workshop made him a toe-clip that pulled the ball of his foot up a bit which gave him the appearance of a Turkish man, but it did the trick.

One of the most precious moments of my entire time in the centre was when I stood at the gate and watched Shotorbabu walk back to the building, along the corridors and back to his bed with only a walking stick by him which was used more for a guide than a prop. That evening he got the harmonica out and sung the evening away which was a great sign of his happiness. Directly after the stroke he said he would never sing again.

I did not sing that evening, but I listened proudly knowing that I had helped to bring back his voice just as I look back and sense a glowing pride within myself when I think of Fozzil running his own tea shop and sharing his home with his wife and their young daughter. I was aware that I had never been able to step into Holly's shoes when she left and to replace her expertise and strong friendship, but I did not want to do that. I was content with having helped keep up the work in the last stages and was confident that I had not let Holly down.

Chapter 11

Goats' Visiting Hours

Theresa asked me to take a patient for a myelogram. I was briefly told what the test involved and then shown to Salam. I needed no introduction. Salam walked around the centre and was always ready to lend a hand to a less able patient. But today he did not look at all happy: he was terrified.

We, along with a ward orderly, took a babytaxi to the hospital for a 4pm appointment. We waited for an hour and a half in the waiting room until the doctor appeared. I produced the two ampules of injection fluid that Val had given me, only to be told that we needed four. I rang the centre and then sat down again to wait in silence for the delivery: we tried to talk but Salam was too frightened and the orderly spoke no English.

I rushed up to the doctor with all four ampules, but was brushed aside. After all, it was his tea break. The waiting now became unbearable so I wandered off and bought a bag of crisps. I offered them round, but fortunately Salam had already been told that he wasn't allowed to eat prior to the test. I felt awful.

Finally the doctor returned and we were ushered into a spotlessly clean X-ray room. Salam was given a local anaesthetic, then a huge needle was immediately inserted into the spinal canal in the lower back. I was no doctor, but I could not believe the anaesthetic would have taken effect so soon, and Salam's pained expression confirmed my thoughts. The dye that was injected into the spinal cord shows up on the X-ray. I had to let go of Salam's hand to go behind the protective screen, but the orderly was given a gown and allowed to stay with him.

The after-effects of the dye are unpleasant, including severe headaches and nausea. Salam was in considerable pain from the onset of the side-effects by the time the results arrived, showing a blockage just below the neck. An operation was recommended. Salam was over the effects of this test within twenty-four hours, but he was grateful that I had stayed with him throughout.

A week later Salam departed for the Dhaka Medical Hospital for the operation. He came to say goodbye to me as though we were never going to see each other again. I felt so sorry for him when I saw the fear in his eyes and knew that he was worried about being so far from home and his mother, his only living relative. Salam wanted to write to her for reassurance, but knew that she would not be able to read his letter and that having to ask an educated member of the village would only cause more anxiety and pain. I waved Salam off having promised that I would come to see him in a couple of days, and this seemed to bring some relief to his young face.

The next day I actually crossed my fingers at the time when Salam's operation was to be performed: I had grown very fond of the man and could not bear to think of anything going wrong. The operation to remove the cause of the block was risky, and if the surgeon slipped in any way Salam could be left worse off than prior to the surgery, so I was relieved when the news that all had been successful reached me via the telephone. We were not allowed to visit that afternoon, but the following morning I left for the Dhaka Medical Hospital with the head social worker, also called Salam.

It was my first experience of a government run hospital, and I found it to be in grim contrast to the centre. The atmosphere was depressing - the entire hospital lay in semi-darkness, giving it a gloomy feel, though the endless corridors appeared clean. We followed miles of these identical empty corridors to the required ward where ten men lay on beds staring up at the ceiling.

Salam was delighted to see us and wasted no time before complaining about the bad treatment he had received in comparison to the centre. The other Salam went off in search of a nurse, and as I had not seen one uniformed official since arriving I settled down on my patient's bed in anticipation of a long wait. I listened to a storm of complaints about the harsh regime, ranging from unsympathetic nurses to unappetising food. Some of the other men in the ward had joined in, but their comments were not as brutal as Salam's since they had nothing with which to compare their experience of health care. Salam returned within half an hour and confirmed that the operation had been a one hundred per cent success and that discharge was planned in two day's time. The hospital was short of space and liked to send people home as soon as possible in order to free another bed. Salam was being discharged unusually fast because the doctor knew that he would be in good hands and the decision met Salam's firm approval.

Salam tipped out several kinds of pills onto the bed and explained when to take each one. I asked him why the nurse wasn't doing this and he told me that the hospital does not supply drugs that are prescribed as part of a patient's treatment and expects each individual to buy their own. Salam knew how fortunate he was to be receiving the financial help of the centre in the purchase of his painkillers and antibiotics. Others were not so well off: the next bed along from the one where I was sat was empty, but only the night before had been occupied by the father of six children. His family could not afford the necessary drugs to prevent infection and he died from neglect. The man in the corridor let out a steady wail from the pain in his stomach where it had been recently operated upon, but he knew he had to grin and bear it as no one was going to the pharmacy to buy any painkillers for him.

I felt cruel just listening to and watching all of the men without lifting a finger to help, but if I were to buy painkillers for the wailing men I would have to buy everyone's prescriptions. I was relieved to hear later on that Salam had given his companion half of his painkillers to allow him a few hours rest. Salam's bravery was easier to understand once I understood that most Bengalis are grateful to receive any help as there are barely any free medical services on offer.

We said our farewells to Salam for the next two days. On our way out of the ward I saw a tiny office for the nurses where three of them sat nattering away. From their position they could not see any of the beds or hear any of the cries of pain or of requests for bedpans. The system seemed to be slap-dash and badly designed, and to me the nurses seemed indifferent exudors of the phrase 'I only work here'.

When I next saw Salam, back in the centre, he was wearing a neck collar to protect the large, unsightly scar that ran from mid-neck to between his shoulder blades. I spent the greater part of his afternoon back talking with him about his relief that the worst was over. Salam must have guessed that I was getting hungry because he produced a packet of crisps for us to eat. What made his gesture even more touching was that he had remembered the type I had bought whilst waiting for the dreaded myelogram and had bought the same again so that we could share them this time.

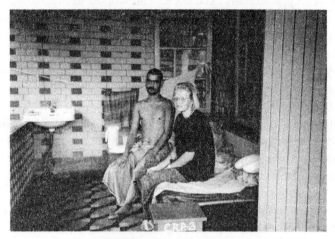

Salam and the author

A few days later Farid and I pushed Ashraf on his bed to the eye specialist hospital which was actually just around the corner from Farmgate, but seemed like the other side of Dhaka. The commotion we caused was immense. Traffic and pedestrians stopped to see the extraordinary sight, made more interesting by our steering which left much to be desired.

Ashraf was fifteen and had fallen from a tree two years previously. After his initial treatment in the centre he was sent home, only to be re-admitted with severe pressure sores just over a year later. The sores had developed because his family had not taken proper care of him and not turned him. One morning Rhina, one of the nurses doing a general health check, discovered that he had lost his sight in his left eye and only had partial vision in his right.

There were long and disorderly queues in the hospital, so we joined what we hoped was the correct one, which it wasn't. After some time wasted in this one we joined the right queue at the back, or at least where we thought the back was. But finally a doctor came out and recognised Farid from his previous visits with Ashraf, as a result of which we were shunted into another queue and shortly called forward into a crowded room where half a dozen people were all having eye tests at the same time. The doctor then took us into a VIP air-conditioned and carpeted consulting room to examine Ashraf's eyes properly. The doctor had worked in Manchester for ten years and was keen to get an update on the National Health Service, joking that with Thatcher in power he was just as well off working in Dhaka despite the conditions.

We were in and out of the hospital in record time, and Farid was pleased that I had come because of the speed of the VIP treatment we had received. I felt wrong attracting special treatment because of the colour of my skin, but what could I do? I comforted myself in the knowledge that I was helping Ashraf, so the carpet was not entirely for me. When we had completed the hair-raising journey back we had to take Ashraf to a new bed on the balcony because he had caught mumps and needed to be in isolation. The poor boy became very depressed, though he still managed to enjoy the odd game of Connect Four which helped to pass the time while he was too ill for his school work.

Another patient who had to have specialised treatment in a private hospital was Omar Ali. He had been involved in a motor accident and had been brought to the centre on a wooden trailer pulled by his brother riding a bicycle. In any other country I think the injured person would have died en route, but in the true Bengali fashion Omar Ali clung on to life. He then needed an operation to stop his internal bleeding caused by a peptic ulcer. The ironic thing was that having had the operation he was cared for afterwards excellently in all areas other than the essential periodical turning over. The staff at the hospital refused to 'waste their time' turning patients, even after Theresa, Salam, Rhoman and countless others had tried to explain its importance. The best arrangement they could agree on was for two members of our staff to go there and turn him themselves.

I went to collect Omar in the ambulance with Theresa and Khokon. The discharging procedure took the best part of two hours and involved filling out a lot of papers which were then added to the mess of a filing system. The hospital bill was very expensive, coming to £125, but sadly even this costly treatment could not save Omar. He battled on for ten days in a critical state, but eventually let go. The doctor later let on that he feared the cause of Omar Ali's death was actually due to a miss-match of the donated blood. In England this would never happen because there are such vigorous checks on each bag of blood before transfusions occur.

There was some embarrassment experienced in this case because apart from the brother who admitted Omar, his family had not wanted him to stay at the centre when they realised how ill he was. His mother had wanted to take her son home to die in peace, but was gently persuaded by the staff at the centre to leave him there to give him a chance of surviving. The family believed that it was all Allah's wish and therefore the consequences of the accident should be played out with no interference. After his death the body was removed in an open lorry and taken back to the village, but for his mother it was too late.

Chapter 12

Code Of Conduct

Brother Joseph is an Italian Xvarian Brother who has lived in Bangladesh for thirty years and now considers himself to be Bengali. The Xvarian brotherhood spend their time finding and helping people less fortunate than themselves; as I have said before, it was Brother Joseph who found Jobeda. He had been involved with the centre from the very beginning, and many of the people he sees receive treatment from Valerie.

One morning Brother Joseph asked me if I would like to visit a Bengali run Christian school for the blind, and I leapt at the opportunity. I followed Joseph through Dhaka listening to a brief history of the school. It was opened by an English woman who spent fifteen years running the school before going back to England. Joseph said that it had been a happy school, but now it was more like a prison, and he expressed concern about the fate of the centre when Valerie finally retires and leaves her empire in the hands of the locals. But I was confident that Valerie would find the right people and train them to continue and replicate her good work, down to the finest detail.

On arrival we were greeted with huge smiles and warm hugs from a line of girls who were delighted to have Joseph visit them again. They all wore a blue and white uniform and as soon as they heard a member of staff arrive they fell silent again. I was given a guided tour by one of the female teachers and in every classroom the pupils were asked either to recite a piece of English poetry or sing to me. I felt a mixture of uneasiness and honour. I was also shown the beautiful rugs and baskets that the girls are taught to make.

We met one very brave girl who had an horrific tale to tell. It was hard not to stare at her as she spoke because she had no eyes and a grossly disfigured face with one ear. Two years ago, back in her village, she was engaged to a man that her parents had agreed on. But soon after a more wealthy man asked the father for permission to marry his daughter and his request was granted. The first loved one was so angry that he lay in wait for the girl as she walked back from school and threw acid in her face. The local doctor advised that she be left to die, but thankfully Brother Joseph found her in time and organised for extensive plastic surgery. Her hands were also mutilated as she had thrown them up to her face to protect her eyes. The tragedy was that the blinded girl not only lost both men, but lost her parents as well because they disowned her. She was, however, now studying for an exam to become a qualified teacher for the blind and will then be employed by the school.

Brother Joseph then took me to visit two young girls who were recovering from open-heart surgery. The hospital was a sprawling mess with people in every nook and cranny. When we reached the ward I was appalled to see at least fifty people in there, all suffering from different ailments. The two girls we visited lay side by side with little protection from their neighbour's goat sniffing at their wounds.

I spoke to the surgeon who had performed their operations, and he explained that the hospital had the equipment and knowledge to carry out such intricate and technical operations, but the after-care was so poor that the patients had little chance of surviving. It was easy to believe this as I looked around the place and I crossed my fingers for the two little pale girls. Sadly, they did not pull through.

On our way back to the centre we called in on an ex-patient of the centre who suffered from polio. The sixteen year old girl was on her own at home and immediately asked us to sit down, which is a sign of acceptance. Our young hostess was very keen to sing and dance with me, but we were pushed for time so before I was allowed to leave I had to promise to return at another date. I never did get the chance to go back, which was a shame, but I did manage to enjoy another evening of singing.

Holly, Brother Joseph and myself all had dinner with a family who lived in a brick house built near the centre on a muddy and rutted road. The four children brought out their harmonica and sung several songs to us, and then it was our turn. Fortunately, Holly is a musician so she played and we sang a few hymns and pop songs. Holly then played the Frere Jacques tune, which is internationally known. Brother Joseph sang in Italian, the girls in Bengali, Holly in French and myself in English. After our sing-song we were invited to the table for a meal, but we were not joined by the family. They stood around the table watching us, making me feel uncomfortable until Joseph explained that it is usual for the people of the house not to eat with their guests unless they belong to the middle or upper classes. I was given the address of their aunt who lives in the East End of London and asked to visit her on my return home.

Another home that I visited with Brother Joseph was part of a large complex of makeshift homes built from tin, sacking and wooden boards. It was amusing to go into one of these homes only to find myself in a well-lit room with electricity, a television and video. I was even urged to watch a video of the man's daughter's wedding. It was strange to be sitting in a single-roomed house that reminded me of the camps my brother and I used to make in the garden and to be surrounded by modern technology.

I walked back to the centre with Joseph and for part of the way we struggled to keep our balance walking along narrow mud paths built up above the level of what smelt and looked like an open sewer. Deep, open ditches ran along the edges of the houses, holding black stagnant water that sometimes gushed into the houses during the annual floods. It was easy to see why disease was rife.

For all this, Bengalis are clean people and are forever washing themselves and their clothes. I still have a vivid memory imprinted on my mind of a man standing knee deep in thick, dark-coloured water, madly rubbing gleaming white shampoo into his hair. It seemed a waste of time when you could see in what he was going to rinse his hair. Along all of the rivers are washing villages, where the local women gather to wash their clothes and household linen. It is quite a spectacular sight, seeing rows of women pounding their brightly coloured clothing up and down on flagstones, miles of washing line behind them dripping with drying cloth of every shade of colour in the spectrum.

There are eight thousand kilometres of navigable riverway in Bangladesh: the country lies in the combined delta of many rivers and hundreds of streams. Most people only know about Bangladesh from the horrific floods that occur during the months from May to October. Every year about one third of the cultivated area is flooded, and this amounts to some seven million acres. The Buriganga River runs through the Chowkbazar area of Old Dhaka, which is made up of small shops, stalls, and crumbled homes in narrow and winding streets. The river is teeming with traffic that connects all of the river fronts in the country with Dhaka.

In my third week in Bangladesh I enjoyed an afternoon of a lifetime when I hired a small banana boat for an hour to watch life go by and admire the congested madness of the Sadarghat ferry terminal from a relatively safe and quiet position. The banks were lined with bamboo houses built on stilts, perched above the river. Children played happily underneath and several swam out to get a better look at me. Two cheeky boys even clambered onto my boat, but the punter pushed them off pretty sharply. Even though other boats constantly passed me and I could hear the cries of fishermen selling their catch, boat owners trying to capture passengers and horns blowing everywhere, it did seem quiet on the river when I thought of the constant cacophony of the Dhaka streets.

I joined several British students on a day's outing on a motored boat. They were on holiday visiting their parents who worked on aid projects and in the High Commission. We chugged further away from the heart of Dhaka and as we did so we noticed that the ferries were getting fewer and small cargo boats were replacing them. I found it refreshing to spend a day away from the centre and with people of my own age. Mike was one of the crowd of twelve on the boat and had initially introduced me to the others after helping me keep my wits about me during the marathon swim. He leant over the boat to bargain for three watermelons from a man on a small banana boat passing us by. The man was sitting on the huge pile of fruit which looked dangerously like it might topple over at any minute; fortunately it did not. As we sat munching our lunch and admiring the colourful sails made up of patches of varying coloured cloth Mike and I remembered an embarrassing episode from the night before.

We were returning to our respective homes in the early hours of the morning after an extraordinary evening in a supposed French cafe. There are a few restaurants that serve western food (with curry flavouring), and also this one cafe where old and scratched jazz records were played. We thought the experience would make a nice

change from fish curry eaten in a grotty restaurant. On our way back
we seemed to be alone on the road, the only noise was the phut-phut
of the babytaxi engine reverberating around the empty and dark
streets. Forgetting where we were for a brief moment we kissed
within the shelter of the babytaxi, much to the amusement of the
driver. However, a nearby policeman was not so entertained by our
behaviour. We had forgotten to respect the culture of our hosts and
were severely reprimanded for so doing.

I had learnt my lesson and when on the boat the others sunbathed
in only swimming costumes I preferred to stay covered up in
accordance with the Muslim code of conduct. This sparked off an
argument with them concerning the matter, but I defended the idea
that we should respect the Muslim way (to no avail). They were also
drinking beer in the open and throwing cans in the river, both of
which I knew would offend the Muslims and would not help the
pollution problem already faced by Bangladesh. Despite our small
differences we continued to have fun together in the evenings, but
when I was back at the centre I was secretly relieved to be amongst
people who I could rely on not to embarrass me.

The only other time that I went on a boat was to get from
Sadarghat ferry terminal to a tiny island in the middle of the river.
About thirty people sat on the boards of the bottom of the boat
which I judged to be twenty too many. One old and frail-looking
man surprised me by rowing us the quarter of a mile to the island.
When we disembarked we had to hand over 3 Taka to the 'Immigration Officer'. Farid explained that the money was a form of tax
and this made me laugh. Despite being within sight of the shore on
both sides of the river, the island was quiet. Only bicycles and
rickshaws were allowed on the tracks. Farid had taken me to visit
a young girl whose health was rapidly declining from being fit
although in a wheelchair, to a critical state, due to the pressure sores
that had developed from neglect.

We were too late.

Brother Joseph took me to a picturesque village called Gepara. On
the way we looked in on a small home for the mentally handicapped
run by the sisters of Mother Theresa. It was a depressing place with
a few bedraggled children staring into space who had been left in

the yard since morning. One scrawny girl clung to my legs like a monkey and would not let go. I found it all terribly heart-rendering and was pleased to get away and continue with the last bit of the journey by rickshaw. Gepara was the first village that I had visited and reading back on my diary I now remember how thrilled I was to leave Dhaka behind me for a few glorious hours of peace. "WOW! Was it nice to get out of Dhaka. The peace, fresh air and space were very welcome."

The village consisted of a small cluster of simple, but spacious huts built out of river mud and roofed with thatch. They were all white washed and everything was kept neat and tidy and surprisingly clean. I had a quick peak into the school and ended up joining the forty pupils on their tiny benches to listen to a story read out by the oldest pupil in Bengali. I just smiled appreciatively. The children were adorable and all wanted a go at sitting on my lap which they treated like any other child would treat a swing in a play park.

We left Gepara by foot and walked along a path lined with trees. It could have been France until we rounded the corner and saw two rickshaws and their riders who instantly pounced on us and tried to tempt us into a ride. An eighteen year old boy called Aldrin joined us on the path and when we reached the river his two sisters were sitting on the bank. The village was predominantly Christian and everyone seemed to know Joseph well. We boarded a banana boat together and crossed the river to the neighbouring village called Mouthside.

We found the house that was owned by a family who were eagerly awaiting our arrival, for we were bearers of good news: their eight year old daughter had trouble with her heart and urgently needed surgery, and Brother Joseph was able to tell her parents that he had found an American doctor who would perform the operation the following week. We were fed with fresh fruit from the trees and due to their hospitality and the heat I ignored all the previous advice I had been given about not eating the skins of fruit, deciding not to think about the consequences. We left the happy parents and moved on to find the little girl. Along the way to the school Aldrin and his sisters gave me a flora lesson and picked me a bunch of flowers. When we told the girl our news she seemed initially thrilled, until the fear began to show. We could not stay to comfort her because her Maths teacher was standing impatiently in the background.

Aldrin took us back to his house for a superb meal which I coped with more effectively than on the home visit. Whilst the vegetables were cooking I was shown the garden where they had grown, which was well stocked, and the pig, cow and chickens also roamed around. The family were self-sufficient in food and the mother produced a delicious meal. Afterwards Joseph said he was going to the house across the field for his siesta and I was to stay put until he returned. I was a touch lost as to what to do for the next two hours, but I need not have worried.

Aldrin had four sisters in all, who immediately took me by the arm and led me to their bedroom. I sat on the huge bed that they all shared and was very amused when they asked permission before playing with my hair. The colour and fineness of it amazed them. They were staggered that I wore no jewellry, so they lined my arms with bracelets, covered my hair with clips, and hung on necklaces and earrings. When it was time to go they would not let me return the earrings.

Their next treat was to put me in a sari. I had feared this and felt self-conscious when they dressed me in their finest clothes. I was left alone in the room to remove my own clothes and put on the short cotton top that was worn under the sari - it only just fitted me across the shoulders. The girls came back in and quickly dressed me in a long piece of cloth that measured the standard five and a half metres. First of all they wound the cloth around my waist and tucked it in to form pleats and then the remainder was hung over my shoulder. Part of the stomach is always exposed and I felt very aware of my rolls of white flab exposed to everyone. It did not take much to convince me that saris are best worn by those for whom they are designed.

Just before Brother Joseph returned I put my own grubby shalwar kamise back on. At least I was in the type of outfit that was expected of unmarried girls. I went to say goodbye to Aldrin who had spent his siesta drawing me a great picture of a boy harvesting coconuts. Before I was allowed to find Joseph I was given a bulging bag of fresh vegetables and the flowers picked earlier. The father of the house then asked if I would take a photograph of his family, which I did with pleasure. Aldrin took the camera and I took his place in the photo, and was given the latest addition of the family to hold. The dear two month old boy had decided to relieve himself whilst perched on my hip and I had to continue to smile for the camera as I felt my T-shirt dampen.

The child had black charcoal around his eyes, which is a traditional way of keeping evil spirits away. The sad thing is that research has shown that it also is a contributing factor in child blindness. Bengalis are generally guided by the fatalistic view of life which says that there is no individual control over what happens, but each individual is manipulated by supernatural beings. This fatalism leads to traditionalism and a resistance to change. Consequently Bangladeshis are often not impressed when foreigners attempt to prove that hard work can lead to success or that some old traditions, such as the charcoal, can do more harm than good. A common Bengali expression is 'if it was good enough for my ancestors it's good enough for me'. I often heard this phrase, including when I was with this family regarding their child's eyes.

Brother Joseph introduced me to yet another family in Dhaka and within ten minutes, after just one foul cup of cha (tea), I was invited to the daughter's wedding. The invitation was for four consecutive evenings, but I thought two would be enough and asked Holly to join me on these special occasions. We only went to the evenings that concerned the bride. We arrived an hour after the stated time, but were still some of the first guests to be ushered into a marquee where about eighty chairs had been set out in rows.

In the Bengali style everything was running several hours late. As the marquee began to fill up some girls entered and started to sing about the groom and were apparently quite rude about him. We were assured that male friends of the groom would retaliate in a similar way the next day. The music stopped and we tucked into tables loaded with food.

Some hours later a throne of flowers was carried on with the stunning bride seated in the middle. She wore a bright pink sari with thousands of hand-sewn jewels. The turmeric ritual began. First the father, then the mother, followed by the rest of the bride's immediate family put a blob of turmeric on her forehead, and then fed the bride with special rice pudding. To me, it seemed such a simple gesture, but it signified the end of her parents' role as parents.

In our ignorance, Holly and I were shocked when the bride cried out and clung to her family. A helpful visitor sitting next to us explained that the behaviour of the bride was normal and expected. This did not mean that she was not genuinely upset, as she knew she was to be married to a man she had never met or seen before and would from then on be his wife and servant. After the family had finished the ritual all of the guests were invited to do the same, but Holly and I felt awkward, not knowing the bride, so we went home. After everyone else had left, we were later told, three of the bride's closest friends remained behind to paint her body in intricate and beautiful patterns.

The third night was held in a hall and was the actual wedding ceremony. Again we were fed on exquisite food that was served by waiters at small tables. None of our neighbours spoke English so we were able to struggle with our meat in silence. We both found getting meat off a bone with only our right hands a pretty tricky task, and I found the only solution was to sit on my left hand to remove the temptation of using it. At least this time we knew that the done thing was to mix the food together with our fingers and then to roll it into a ball and push it with the thumb into the mouth. The left hand is the dirty hand that is used to wash yourself and replaces the job of toilet paper, and therefore must never touch food.

One morning I needed to go to the toilet badly and had no time to waste. I realised that I had no toilet paper in my bag and could not hang around to find any. I used the staff loo, which was a squatting one and then had the fun task of using the jug of water and my left hand. I achieved the task with ease, but admittedly ended up with wet trousers. On previous occasions staff had laughed when they saw me heading for the bathroom clutching my private loo paper supply because Bengalis, like most Asians, do not use it. This time I had also caused a few smiles because it did not take much imagination to realise what had happened. However, I was not put off by my ineptness and stopped packing my bag with loo paper every morning. At the end I was pretty efficient at toileting the ethnic way, and the habit also made the temptation of eating with my left hand less difficult to resist.

The bride and groom entered from different sides of the room and sat on the raised platform festooned in flowers without even so much as a glance at each other. The bride looked as stunning as before, but Holly and I could not help feeling sorry for her when we saw the fat groom and his miserable expression. He was allowed to take his first look at his new wife as they exchanged garlands, but the bride remained with her head bowed. A mirror was then placed on the floor in front of them and her veil was hung over both of their heads, and in this way they looked at each other. They were considered to be lucky as they had been allowed two telephone calls to each other: two more than in most arranged marriages. They then fed each other and were officially married.

The bride was now a member of her husband's family and will rarely visit her own parents. Therefore it is essential that her parents are happy that the groom's family are the sort that they would want their daughter to live in. The couple went to live in the groom's house, according to tradition, and the bride's mother-in-law would then begin to train her to be a good wife and to please her husband.

Holly and I both felt very privileged to have been invited and to have had the opportunity to witness such an incredible ceremony.

Chapter 13

Cockroaches - The Night of the Long Knives

I had arrived in Bangladesh during the winter as advised by Valerie because it is the easiest season for foreigners to accustom themselves to. During the day the temperatures range between 70 degrees to 75 degrees F and in the night it tends to drop into the 40's F. The days are mostly dry although I experienced some days of winter rain which comes down in sheets, but compared to the monsoon is nothing.

It was in the middle of February when I sat huddled under a piece of plastic sheeting over my knees and the hood of the rickshaw over my head. The rain still managed to pour down my neck and soak me through to the skin in seconds. The rickshaw boy did not even attempt to cover up and was fairly amused by the pathetic picture I portrayed. When I arrived at the centre I joined everyone in the office. The centre seemed to have shrunk in size and everywhere indoors felt cramped.

Of course the usable space had shrunk because the yard was out of use due to the rain. At the best of times we were all cramped into a small space and had to cope with difficulties in the layout of the building such as the stairs. A patient from one of the upstairs wards inevitably had to come down at some stage which caused a palava. The stairs were quite steep and rounded a corner which made navigating wheelchairs and bodies down to the bottom a skilled job that also required strength. In the process the chairs sometimes knocked the walls chipping off paint and generally making a mess of the rented house which, understandably did not please the landlord. We had somewhat given up worrying with only a matter of weeks left until the lease ran out and still with nowhere to go.

With the rain pouring down outside most patients opted for staying in bed. During the monsoon the staff are not so wet, but on that day everyone knew the rain would only last a couple of hours rather than months as in the monsoon. Consequently the staff took the easy way out as well. I joined Theresa in reorganising the nurses' notes in all the individual files. The nurses tended to stash away each additional test result, graph or set of notes in any order so long as it was in the correct file. We devised a system whereby all of the separate categories could be seen at once which made searching for a specific item a whole lot easier and quicker. I found it a most enlightening project as it gave me the chance to read through the notes and learn about each patients case history.

In the afternoon the clouds cleared away and after a morning with everyone cooped up in doors I was more than ready to get outside for some 'fresh air'. Wendy and I walked past some cleaners who were arguing over a task that had been set by Valerie. It was obvious that no one wanted to do it. We established that all the bed side lockers had to be emptied and cleaned in preparation for the big move to the new site which was still an imaginary plot in every-one's mind. Without thinking about it we told the cleaners to stop squabbling and to let us do the job as we had no other pressing engagements. Some kind people tried to put us off and others refused to let a Badeshi (white foreigner) do such filthy work. It was this attitude that decided it and we went off in search of buckets and mops.

First of all we carefully cleared out all of the personal belongings which in most cases were pitifully few. I remembered back to when I had gone into hospital laden down with books, tapes, food and anything else I had been able to lay my hands on. Most lockers contained a plastic comb, a piece of long-since-forgotten-about fruit and a few crumbled cigarettes.

We hauled the lockers out into the yard and then the fun really begun. We had the scrubbing brushes near by, but what we had forgotten was a machete. An army of huge cockroaches came charging out of each locker in all directions. They were the size of a mouse and had the uncanny tendency to stay alive against all odds. We stamped on them, ran them over with wheelchairs and tried stabbing them with a knife borrowed from the kitchen. At the end of our hour long battle there were about twenty dead, a dozen wounded and many more escaped, and I did not dare to think about where to.

During the battle I started to sing the song Rasputin by Boney M, but I think the words about how he would never die were lost on the small audience that had gathered to watch the fiasco and were certainly lost on our enemy. The afternoons amusement was not over for the clever cockroaches had a back up battalion of maggots that were feasting on the sticky mess left by the rotting fruit. Thankfully they were no competition for us warriors!

Talking of maggots, I was told a very nasty story which made my stomach turn. A patient had fallen out of his wheelchair and broken his already paralysed arm. A plaster cast was put on the arm and the patient actually thought he was lucky because he had no sensation in his arm anyway. A few weeks later he began to feel ill and was convinced that it was something to do with the plaster. It may have been an advantage not to have been able to feel the breaking of his bone, but the loss of his sensation also meant that he had to wait until the little maggots that had been feasting on his flesh were so full that their host began to feel ill. When the Doctor cut the cast off he exposed a nibbled arm that had begun to rot. YUK, I never want to break my arm. The patient had managed to raise the alarm just in time to save his arm which slowly healed with treatment.

Wendy and I had been executing the cockroaches just outside the kitchen that consisted of one room with a small fire and a large cooking pot that looked just like the picture story cauldron. I was worried that the escaped 'roaches might have found their way into the big black cooking pot and would be served to innocent people. Surely they would be dead?! I went into the kitchen for the first time, but could see no cockroaches or witches, only the dedicated cook stood by the fire. He miraculously churned out edible meals three times a day for one hundred people. He was not unduly worried about any cockroaches and continued to prepare a vegetarian meal.

Twice a day patients receive curried vegetables and rice in large portions and in the morning they are served something lighter and cold. The meals are vegetarian as a norm because meat is too expensive, yet on special occasions everyone happily tucks into a fish or chicken dish. All staff have to pay for their meals if they decide to eat at the centre so most of them bring their own lunch if they live too far away to go home in the three hour rest period.

Many of the patients have a tastier and more nourishing diet whilst at the centre and are genuine when they say they will miss the hospital food when discharged. As with all the daily activities, the patients are encouraged to help in the preparation of the vegetables and as they do so are given guidance as to what a healthy diet is and how to cut the costs of their food by using the wonder bags and other tricks of the trade.

At lunch times there was sometimes a small fire alight in the back yard, around which a number of women would be gathered. They were being shown how to cook from a wheelchair, but at the same time they were educated on the subject of preparing healthy meals and how to save money. This was based on the 'wonder bag'.

Every patient, male or female, is sent home with a wonder bag that they have made in the occupational therapy department. It is a bag filled with crumbled pieces of polystyrene from packing boxes, and is used for insulation. Each person is taught to only half-cook their pot of rice and then to take it off the fire and place the pot in the bean bag. Because the heat is retained the rice continues to cook while the fire can be put out. Thus precious fuel is saved. All of the patients grumble and say that they don't want one because they don't think it will work or save them money. But more often than not they return for their outpatient appointment or wait until a home visit and put in an order for more wonder bags at a cost of 10 Taka (20p) for other members of their village.

I was at the centre during Ramzan which is the ninth month of the Muslim year. Fasting is the third pillar of Islamic observance and is considered a compulsory duty during Ramzan. From sunrise to sunset fasting is obligatory, but during the night eating is allowed. Drinking any form of liquid is forbidden and some extremists will not even allow themselves to swallow their own saliva which must be very testing during the heat of the day. Everyone plans evening parties and large meals during Ramzan and consequently little sleep is had. Ill people are exempt from fasting as well as pregnant women, the aged, children and travellers. However, they are expected to make it up during the following year if possible.

The staff appeared bleary eyed in the mornings from lack of sleep, but although they could not eat during the day they certainly made up for it in the evenings and probably consumed more calories than usual. They caught up on their sleep during the siesta which meant they missed torturing themselves by watching the patients, volunteers and non-Muslims eating their lunch. I certainly could not have stopped drinking water through the day, but I was fully prepared never to drink a Fanta, Sprite or Coke again. In every village, however remote, and on every corner, fizzy drinks were sold and as I could not drink the local water I consumed rather a lot of them.

I asked Salam to explain the reasons behind Ramzan which he did by giving me an article to read from The Bangladesh Times, one of two papers printed in English. It read;

"Ramzan, above all, teaches us that we should try and check our lustful impulses for our own good as well as for the public weal. This is one lesson we must all adhere to assiduously for saving our souls and saving society and the nation from eventual ruination at a time when symptoms of social degeneration appear all pervasive...Time has come to rebuild resistance against this deluge towards a dangerously degenerate and self-centred society so that the finer human qualities may prevail. Religion points the way to our salvation."

In March the tree in the yard bore its fruit called Kul, a small green and bitter berry. It is a very popular fruit and the Ayahs were often seen pulling down the branches so that everyone could help themselves to a handful of the berries to snack on. Sometimes patients and staff alike bashed at the tree with a broom handle to knock the fruit down. The rules at the Centre made it illegal to do this because of the mess it left on the ground and the damage it caused the tree. The leaves and squashed berries made the ground slippery which could be lethal for any unsteady person practising their first few steps. The only time that the fruit was allowed to be eaten was when it had fallen to the ground naturally.

I tried to be very careful about what I ate because I had heard the usual run of the mill stories about travellers ending up in a dodgy hospital rigged up to a rusty-looking drip. Despite my efforts I did not escape the dreaded upset stomach. I happily drunk Val's tea which was made in the usual way with boiled water. Others did not risk it because the water had not been boiled for ten minutes like it says it should be in all the guide books. I was fortunate that I did not have to use any of the water purification tablets that I had bought with me because at home there was always properly boiled water in the fridge and away from home I preferred the fizzy drinks to swimming pool water which is what the tablets taste of.

I made a point of only eating freshly cooked hot food so that there ⁓o chance of any nasty microbes being able to breed and fruit that ⁓ ⁚been peeled (apart from when in Mouthside). Nevertheless I came down with violent diarrhoea and vomiting for four days. I thought of sending the rules into a dieting agency when I weighed myself and discovered that I had lost over a stone in four days and all I had done was lie in bed, sit on a loo, and lean over a bucket feeling extremely sorry for myself. On the second day I managed to totter over to a chemist and purchase some excellent anti-nausea tablets. I had to buy each tablet individually, not by the bottle as in Boots. It was simple enough for me because I only needed a few, but I imagined Theresa going off to buy the week's supply of medication for the centre - she would have to spend all day counting the tablets.

A mosquito bit me on the lip and the next day I was graced by a huge septic boil on my face. The climate encouraged infection and had certainly done a good job on me. I was so embarrassed going back into the centre that I pretended Holly had hit me. The poor girl spent the day defending herself and convincing people of her innocence.

I had first hand experience of a Bangladeshi dentist when I chipped a front tooth. The dentist capped the tooth for me, causing me no pain, and when he had finished his handiwork I could not tell which tooth he had been working on. I had the choice of all shades of cement, from sparkling white to nicotine yellow or rotten black. Needless to say I chose a shade from the white end of the scale. The tooth still looks perfect to this day and the whole thing only cost me £3.

Chapter 14

A Rusty Introduction to Nursing

Theresa faces a daunting job at the centre. The organisation Voluntary Service Overseas (VSO) is sponsoring Theresa for two years to teach the staff specialised care for the disabled. Even the trained nurses need extra training because they are not exposed to it in their hospital training scheme run by the government. The fifteen orderlies and Ayahs have no training at all. They do not need to know about the medical care, but it is essential that they know why they have to turn the patients and how to do so safely.

The human spine is actually quite fragile and if a person lifts heavy weights incorrectly they are putting themselves into immediate danger of straining their own back and, as Holly explained, most of the staff had done just that. Once Holly started the staff treatment rota many orderlies stepped forward and admitted that they suffered from back pain. They had kept quiet because they thought it was part and parcel of the job and would certainly not have dreamt of seeking help from the overworked staff. Holly happened to see an orderly wince in pain when lifting a patient and insisted on checking him over.

Another outcome was Theresa's lifting classes which all staff had to attend - even the two trained physiotherapists had been lifting badly. In her first class I offered to be the dummy to experiment on. I thought it was quite a brave move as at one stage I found myself in the air with my head below the level of my legs with eight hands clutching my four limbs and no one supporting my head. Theresa timetabled more lessons for the future when she saw how far they had to go. I am heavier than the average Bengali and at first everyone moaned at the thought of having to lift me, but we managed to prove that if you lift in the proper way no human can be too heavy. The patients also benefited from the lifting lessons because their bodies could now be kept straight with complete support.

I told Theresa that I had a place at Middlesex hospital in London to do my RGN (Registered General Nurse) training when I returned to England. She was excellent at teaching me things like how to give injections, take blood pressures and how to record fluid balance charts. In fact Theresa set me to work on the fluid balance charts with the excuse that it was good practice for night duty in London. One of her favourite phrases was "Don't do it like this at the Middlesex, they'll crucify you, but we have to improvise here." She once boasted that I would not have to do my training when she had finished with me, but then I felt quite put out when a few weeks later Theresa said she did not think I would enjoy nursing. How right she was! After a year at Middlesex I gave up and applied to do a degree in Occupational Therapy at St Loyes College in Exeter. I have been given a place in September 1992 which is why I now have a year in which to write a book and return to the centre.

Some of the local staff were also very keen that I should gain some nursing experience and get a taste of what was to come. On one hot day in March Rhaman made me watch a mini operation which took place outside in the yard next to the showers. The patient was Abdul Nuor who was only thirteen and had had a road accident and snapped his spine, resulting in paralysis from his waist down. He had a huge pressure sore on his buttock which was very deep and was not healing.

Rhaman performed the operation without any protective clothing on and the word 'sterile' was foreign to him. Maybe that is a bit cruel because all of the equipment used is boiled first and he did wear a pair of rubber gloves when he plunged his hand into the sore which was so deep that his entire hand disappeared. Rhaman's aim was to dig out all of the dead tissue to allow new and healthy tissue to grow in its place. Abdul Nuor did not need any anaesthetic as he had no feeling below his waist. Having no feeling did not prevent him from looking worried and he still had a sense of smell which at the time was a major disadvantage for anyone within the immediate area.

Abdul Nuor was more commonly known as Mr Topi because he had knitted himself a red hat (which translated into Bengali is Lal

Topi). Mr Topi wore his hat day in and day out, whatever the weather. I had to retire from the 'operating theatre' because for the first time I really thought I was going to vomit or faint and the whole procedure seemed so brutal.

Another procedure I had to watch was the insertion of a pair of skeletal tongs. A recently admitted patient had his head shaved and was then given an anaesthetising injection above the ear on both sides of his head. Both areas swelled up into impressive lumps which indicated that the time had come for the gruesome part. I was asked to hold the patient's head to prevent any flinching, but I still believe that Rhoman had an ulterior reason for asking me to do it, which was to keep me there throughout and not let me wimp away again.

As it was, I was fine this time and was happy to help. The first pair of tongs that Rhaman uncovered had gone rusty at the tips, but thankfully they were not used and another pair were found that were sparkling clean all over. Rhaman started to screw the ends into the skull: they only went in a few millimetres, but it was enough to hear the crunching of the bone. Because of the near proximity to the ear the sound was amplified for the patient so I was asked to speak encouraging words to him. What good my talking in English did I do not know, but the procedure was soon over and he had survived the experience. Before we could tidy up a weight was attached to the tongs to prevent any movement.

Mr Topi also developed scabies which had spread to two other patients by the time it was detected by Wendy. With her hard work, Wendy prevented it spreading any further and within two weeks of treatment the infected three were given the all-clear. Every morning Wendy had to clean the patients with a prescribed solution from head to toe paying particular attention to the areas under the finger and toe nails which are ideal places for infection to breed. Wendy's morning ritual took four hours and then the sheets all had to be washed separately too.

Flies swarmed the centre. During the day it was sometimes difficult to see the sheets on the beds for the flies which liked to settle on open wounds, urine drenched sheets and buckets of old dressings, scraps of food and other such delights that were left under each bed until an orderly arrived to empty them every other hour. Flies are disgusting and off-putting anywhere, but in a hospital environment they are a menace because they carry infection from one person to another, and in the heat they were especially hard to eradicate.

Incontinence is a great problem the centre has to face. Ninety per cent of newly admitted patients are both urine and faeces incontinent as a result of damaged nerves in the bowel and bladder. Part of every patient's treatment is to be taught how to control their own bladders so that they are no longer incontinent, a problem which can ruin a person's confidence and social life. They are taught to take note of what they have drunk and to keep a time-check. Although their bladders are paralysed the patients learn how to feel their abdomen and to judge how full their bladder is by the extent of its distension. It does not take long for an individual to learn how often they must push down on their bladders with their hands to expel their urine. For instance, it is almost as rare for one of the disabled members of staff to have an accident as it is for me.

The problem is that it is very hard to push out all of the urine and any that is left in the bladder for a long time can become infected. This can lead to kidney failure. The centre has boxes full of donated catheters, but they too cause trouble. By inserting a catheter into the bladder you are making another opening into the body that is extremely prone to infection, therefore catheters are only used in severe cases like those of patients in striker beds. When male patients are in their initial stage of care they lie on plastic-covered sheets with their hips raised so that the penis hangs down. Each time they pass urine it collects in the dip and is then frequently cleared away by the cleaners. Unfortunately, it can never be frequent enough to prevent the flies from gathering. Females have to be toileted in their separate bathroom by an Ayah.

There are patients who are not incontinent who are all supposed to have a bright yellow plastic bottle called a 'chungi' with them at all times. They didn't, and their desperate cries, "Sister, chungi!" became very familiar. I used to rush off in a mad search for one of the revolting bottles, but other staff made the patient learn the hard way and find one for themselves. I preferred to take the option of running myself than clearing up a puddle.

Each patient had to own a pair of shoes to walk in because lack of sensation and movement in paralysed legs can easily lead to accidents to feet through cuts and burns that may go unnoticed for some days. Many patients had never worn shoes previously and were not keen to start. If the patient did not own a pair of shoes or could not afford to pay for one, the centre could usually provide.

A little old lady called Joytun Bibi practised doggedly on the parallel bars every day, much more than the required amount. She was practising her walking and turning in barefoot and we all knew that she would eventually have to get used to shoes. One morning Wendy took Joytun Bibi out on her low-level trolley along the busy city road to the nearest Bata shoe shop. The poor lady was stared at by all, terrified of the traffic, the blasting horns of lorries, the babytaxis, overloaded buses and the gliding by of a businessman's limousine. A crowd quickly drew around, her time came to try on a pair of plimsolls for size, with special help given by the shop-keeper. Wendy and Joytun Bibi returned to the centre triumphantly holding their parcel. From then on the brand new plimsolls and socks were kept proudly on display by her side when not in use (which was most of the time) for all to see, as their owner was honoured that something had been bought just for her.

There was a sensible rule at the centre which stated that volunteers should not buy presents for patients. It could give the impression that all foreigners were well off, which I suppose we were in comparison. However, many volunteers were living on a very tight budget having financed their travel and living expenses from hard-earnt savings, and presents could also lead to jealousy and impossible demands. So the giving of gifts had either to come through the centre as if coming from general funds (which was how Wendy produced the plimsolls), or to be made clear that it was an exception for a special occasion such as departure or birthdays.

Jamal was a patient in ward one who had been involved in a road accident when he was a bus driver on the Dhaka Syhlet Route. He was a good-looking man, but had one grotesquely damaged eye from the accident. His pretty wife came to visit him regularly at the centre and each time he wished he could cover his unsightly eye. Wendy loved spoiling people and prior to being aware of the rule regarding gifts went out and bought Jamal a pair of dark glasses because she knew he was too poor to be able to afford them himself.

The optician gave her a generous discount when he heard that they were for a patient from the centre. Jamal was delighted with his present and was more relaxed when his wife next visited.

Upstairs there was a large cupboard full of donated clothes, mainly from Westerner. The children were happy to wear shirts and skirts, but the women only wore saris. Some men wore trousers, but again most of them preferred what they were used to, lunghis. These were large pieces of cloth with one seam that were worn around the waist, pleated and tied in a knot, so that they fall like a straight skirt and can be worn at any length. Any donated clothes that would not be worn were cut up so that the cloth, zips and buttons could be used again. In this way the centre was able to provide every patient with an outfit if they could not afford to do so themselves.

Some patients grew accustomed to their new luxury surroundings and became quite spoilt in their manner of behaviour. The centre was equipped with electricity and fans, three meals a day were served, and in theory each patient had a bed to themselves. The living standards were much better than most patients were used to at home. In the yard there was a reconstruction of a village hut which was built so that patients could spend their last week living in it to get used to living in their normal habitat from a wheelchair and to gain a little independence. Because the centre is frequently overflowing people are always allocated beds in the hut, whether it is their last week or not. I remember a man being told he had to vacate his bed in a downstairs ward and go to the hut. He moaned that it had no fan and was very cramped and hence had to be reminded that it was very much like his own home to which he would soon be returning.

Chapter 15

A Pint Of Blood

In early March a very ill young man with a broken neck arrived at the centre. He had lost a large quantity of blood from internal haemorrhaging and needed a blood transfusion immediately, but there was no blood in stock in the small pathology lab. To make matters worse he belonged to the blood group AB negative, which is the rarest type. The majority of Bengalis belong to the group B positive, but one member of staff also belonged to AB negative and donated a pint, which is the maximum amount allowed in one go. A brave and relatively healthy patient also gave a pint, but it was not enough.

Valerie went on the radio to plead for donors, but no one came forward. Valerie did not seem surprised by the negative response because it had happened many times before. Doctor Soames is an English Doctor who runs the British hospital and gives a great deal of his time to the centre. He found a patient from his files who was willing to give the extra vital pint. Sadly the patient only lived for another week and although Valerie's success rate is exceptionally high there are always the unfortunate few who slip through the net.

The positive outcome of the tragic death was that Valerie organised for a specialist team to come to the centre to take blood from any willing healthy person. As I lay on the bed watching my rich red blood being drawn out of my arm a small dispute was in progress between Valerie and Mohua. Valerie wanted to donate some blood, but Mohua said that she had done so only a few months previously and therefore should not give any more for a while. In Bangladesh people are allowed to donate one pint of blood every three months which is how long it takes the body to replenish what was lost, but in England the time span is six months to be on the safe side. Eventually Valerie gave up her battle and was content with the eleven pints from others.

I had never been a donor before so Swarup tried to calm my nerves by joking that I was only scared in case my blood turned out to be blue or green. In fact it was a pain-free experience and afterwards we were rewarded with a bottle of Fanta and a biscuit to restore our energy. With my boost of energy I helped to stock the fridge in the pathology lab with the bags of blood and when all were safely labelled and stored the stock looked healthily full again, and hopefully would stay that way.

I was continuously amazed by the strength in the patients and their obvious will to live. Some people arrived at the centre in the most appalling conditions and to have even survived the journey was a miracle. They frequently travelled long distances on rickety trailers or rickshaws over bumpy surfaces and against all odds still managed to pull through. Yet having said that, I also encountered the other extreme where people just gave up and let nature take its cause because they believed everything was the work of Allah.

I was taken to a huge and ultimately depressing slum along the railway track near to Farmgate by Brother Joseph. I was confronted by a sea of people and cardboard boxes, Hessian and plastic sheets that served as homes and rubbish. There were an estimated one million people living in this slum alone. I felt frightened walking through the area and never would have done so on my own.

We picked our way around tiny fires being kept alight by a few pieces of kindling for warmth and so that the women could attempt to make a meal out of the few grains of rice that they had salvaged from the streets and markets. Most of the men and older children were out begging or working in appalling conditions in factories for next to nothing. Within seconds a mass of children had gathered around us and I looked down onto a swarm of big brown eyes and smiles. I could not see what they had to smile about, but maybe they were just content to be alive. Coming from the privileged background that I was brought up in, I found it hard not to think that life for a Bengali is one of continual hardship and struggle leaving them little time to feel sorry for themselves, which these smiles illustrate so well.

I heard a gruelling bloodthirsty scream from a young child and was pushed away fast so that I could not see the cause of the pain. I am glad that I could not because later I was told that the child's mother had maimed her month-old daughter by cutting a hand off so that when she was old enough to go out begging she would gain more sympathy and hopefully collect more money. I felt sick. Brother Joseph noticed a small boy who had a cloudy eye and knew that it was an infection that if left untreated would lead to blindness. He spoke to the mother of the child who refused help on the basis that it was Allah's will for her son to go blind. I found it hard not to think that sometimes we were fighting a losing battle, and indeed whether we had any right to be fighting against an individual's wish as in the case of Omar Ali.

Some tried to fight for themselves, but were stopped through lack of funds and bad organisation. A patient in the centre was suffering from heart trouble and was taken to the government heart hospital. They could not get in for the queues and were told to try somewhere else when they saw a waiting man collapse from a heart attack. Even in his critical condition no doctor was prepared to see him because it was lunch time. Theresa kept the man alive in the back of the ambulance by CPR (cardiac and pulmonary resuscitation) as they sped towards another hospital. Both men survived thanks to Theresa and Khokon's quick thinking and acting.

An infuriating afternoon was spent in the chest hospital. Khokon and I had waited in the hall for twenty minutes having left the patient in the ambulance, which had no circulation of air and was parked in the full glare of the sun. A nurse walked past and was bombarded with questions from the two dozen people who had joined us in the wait. She calmly replied that all of the doctors were on their break and would be back shortly. Khokon had had enough and rightly thought it ridiculous that there should be no one available in a hospital to see sick people, even when they had an appointment. We marched around the hospital, opening closed doors and more often than not being turned away. Finally we found a sympathetic doctor who agreed that it was a bit bad to run a hospital in such a way that everyone had their breaks at the same time and in a time when appointments were made.

In Bangladesh there are one hundred and thirty hospitals with only two thousand registered nurses and eight thousand doctors to serve them. Relative to the population these figures get worse: there is only one doctor for every fifty thousand people, a factor which influences the high infant mortality rate of 135 per 1000 live births. With even fewer nurses it is clear why the after care is so appalling.

Eighty per cent of the population live in rural areas which makes maintaining a good health standard throughout the country virtually impossible. With more and more people migrating to the cities in search of work this should become easier to cope with.

Wendy and I went on a home visit to see Rosina who had been a patient in the centre for seven months with a tumour on her spine, between the sixth and seventh vertebrae. She left the centre still in much pain after an unsuccessful operation in the Dhaka Medical College Hospital. Rosina was still able to move her arms, but was otherwise completely paralysed. As well as being in pain she suffered from spasms. Rosina lived in her grandfather's house and I asked him how old he was, to which he replied one hundred and four - he certainly looked it. It is double the country's average life expectancy of forty-seven, so we did wonder if he could remember when he really was born.

Rosina wrote lovely poems of life in Bangladesh, a life she wished she was still part of. She also taught her brother and sister to read and write. Rosina read us some of her poetry and was visibly delighted that we had taken the time and effort to visit her. I made her a small paper game where the loser had to do a forfeit, which together we wrote out in Bengali. I was devastated to hear that little Rosina died soon after I left Bangladesh.

That evening I went to the BAGHA Club with Holly for a well-earnt pint (we thought so, anyway). We were chatting to a lad of about my age called Jonathan who was doing research on breast-feeding, and told us that he had been to a village where they had never seen a white person before. At first the villagers had been scared of him and were convinced that his camera was a device which would take away their soul. The village was remote, but one or two homes had radios and everyone clustered around them in the evenings to listen to the music. They also heard the advertisements, one of which was for powdered milk. The advert encouraged mothers to feed their infants on it instead of breast-feeding. Many of the young mothers were malnourished themselves and thought it a good idea, especially as it was a product from the 'rich west'. The results have been disastrous.

The milk is mixed up by the mothers with dirty water and in the wrong ratios because they cannot read the instructions. The young babies cannot digest the mixture and consequently their health is affected, sometimes to the extent that they die. Jonathan was mainly doing research for his degree, but could not help giving health education to the local women as he toured the villages. But it is nearly impossible for one person to go to a village and change their ways overnight: some accepted his ideas, others rejected them, and some thought he was mad.

Having enjoyed the western haven and with a cool beer inside us, we left. The rickshaw boys, who are always outside the club, recognised Jonathan, so all three of us got on the one rickshaw. I was the mug who offered to balance on the back, and from my heightened position I could see how the boy was struggling, so I offered to take over. What a laugh it was! I swerved all over the road, and moved only about four metres before collapsing from exhaustion. The rickshaws are amazingly heavy, with wonky steering, and I vowed never to travel three to a rickshaw again out of pity to the peddler.

Whilst I was there the Bangladesh Times printed an article on a report from the government about the possibility of abolishing rickshaws in Dhaka, on the grounds that the roads were too congested. It was their belief that the rickshaws were the crux of the problem. If the new law had gone through, millions of people would have been out of work, and yet more millions would never be able to afford any means of transport. At the time of this debate I was reading an excellent book called The City Of Joy which is all about the life of a rickshaw man in Calcutta. The book made a big impact on me, leaving vivid memories, and it made me realise just how devastating the new law could be to the many struggling families of Bangladesh.

Chapter 16

Eyes On A Streaming Face

Salam and Farid made up the social workers' team and did an excellent job. They were brothers-in-law - Salam's wife is Farid's elder sister. A large percentage of their time was taken up by organising home visits and the Outreach Programme. The centre keeps in touch with all of its ex-patients through a quarterly newsletter, but more importantly by the visits.

Every Wednesday the Outreach Programme is put into action. A team goes to several homes in the Dhaka vicinity in the centre's tempo with its twelve seater cab powered by a motorbike. The team consists of either Farid or Salam, a physiotherapist, nurse, cleaner and a volunteer if they so wish. The medical team assesses each patient and encourages families to listen so that they can learn how to care for their invalid relatives. They don't just check on the patient's mobility, they look for signs of pressure sores and infection, adequate diet and good general hygiene care. The social worker makes sure that they are maintaining their finances and that any walking aid is well cared for. But why does a cleaner go? The idea behind this is to involve all of the staff in the patient's total care and it is hoped that by following a patient's case through to the end the cleaners will be able to provide a better service and understand more about what they are working towards.

The patients who live further away are still visited, but only by one of the social workers, so it is known as a home visit. Farid and Salam go off for up to a week on separate routes, passing through as many ex-patients homes as possible. This takes place roughly every three months. Home visits are also undertaken in the city for patients who have learnt to cope on their own, but need to be checked on once in a while.

My first experience of the Outreach Programme was when we went to see Dolly. The centre's tempo had been converted for disabled drivers and was being driven with expertise by Motin, who was the first person ever to take a disabled person's driving test. The examiner was astonished and almost mocked the idea that anyone who could only operate a tempo with hand controls could gain a driving licence. Since then, more members of staff have taken and passed the exam. But the examiner was not the only sceptic. All petrol stations are self-service so Motin shifted across the front seat to the passengers side and asked the owner if he would help to fill up. The petrol tank is located under the driver's seat in all tempos and they run on diluted petrol. The owner of the garage told Motin to do it himself and just laughed when we told him that Motin could not walk. Above the number plate was a sign that clearly said 'Disabled Driver' in Bengali, but even when he had read it the owner looked bemused.

With a full tank we set off to the outskirts of Dhaka. I didn't notice leaving the city and had to be assured that the place where Dolly lived was a village, but I decided it was a suburb. We got a little lost in the narrow streets, all of which looked identical. I was slightly alarmed when I leant out and saw an open sewer on either side of us, inches away from the wheels. Eventually we parked where the track broadened and continued on foot.

Motin opted to guard the tempo so we left him behind and when we arrived at the address we found Dolly waiting for us. Dolly was ten years old, but would never walk again. Monica, the head nurse, said she was in good health, but Farid was not so pleased. Dolly had been idle with her homework and was falling behind at school. This concerned us because the centre was paying for her education to give Dolly a chance in later life, though it was hard to be cross with someone like Dolly for long.

Many Bengalis are offended if their visitors hurry. The western idea of 'dropping in for a quick cup of coffee' is alien to them - as a guest you are expected to stay for at least an hour, and our visit was no exception. Dolly's family were so excited to be our hosts that her mother had prepared a huge meal. It was my first meal 'in public' and public it certainly was. At least seventy people had flocked around and were staring into the room and cramming into the doorway. No one else seemed to bat an eyelid, but I felt very self-conscious. Bengalis feel secure when surrounded by people and the idea of privacy is incomprehensible. In most lower class homes the whole family sleeps in the same room, with all the females in one bed and all the males in the other. I just wished I could have felt more secure during that meal.

A bowl was passed around and I made my first mistake by washing both hands instead of just my right hand. A plate of innocent looking Dahl was then presented to me, so I gingerly started to make a ball of food with my fingers, all too aware that one hundred and forty eyes were on me. I took a mouthful and thought I had ignited myself in the process. I can eat hot food and enjoy going out for Indian meals, but this was like nothing else I had ever tasted before. My cheeks were burning red and my eyes were pouring with water, but I could do nothing about it. My hostess immediately thought her cooking was not good enough and my host offered a glass of water, which I had to decline as it had come straight from the tap.

I somehow managed to work my way through a polite amount of food, slowing cooking myself in the corner. I totally forgot my initial worries of eating with my right hand - worries which paled into insignificance compared with the pain I was experiencing. After lunch we were shown the sock factory in the yard. Dolly's family made their meagre living by weaving socks using a recently acquired machine. On our way back to the tempo I sarcastically thanked Farid for his moral support through my ordeal: his eyes had been as wet as mine, but from laughing. Farid replied that I should not have such a pathetic mouth and when I told him how I felt about the audience he laughed again and said "You have white hair so you must expect it, but do not be sad because it is a good advert for the centre." By that he meant that the people who had come to watch us asked questions and learnt about the centre.

Our next visit was to a man who greeted us warmly and offered the only chair to me. We had been carting around old biscuit tins all day and now we handed them over. I had no idea why this man would want old tins, but then his brother gave us six beautifully painted tins back. Babul paints the old tins and then the centre sells them and gives him the profits. I asked if I could have a peek inside Babul's house and was taken inside by the proud brother. A step led up the jute-walled and tin-roofed hut, which meant that Babul could not get in without assistance. Babul's young wife stands behind him and lifts him from the wheelchair and up the step before pivoting round to place Babul on his bed. The space between the bed and the wall is too thin to accommodate his wheelchair. I didn't dare to ask what happened when it rained, but I presume Babul has to stay in bed all day.

Babul broke his neck in a diving accident. When he was well on the way to self-independence he moved from his ward in the centre to the hostel which was situated across the road. When he was caring for himself, while remaining under the umbrella of the centre's care, Babul met his wife. With a mind for business Babul bought two second-hand rickshaws which his brothers rode to provide an income. His painting is more of a hobby.

Once a week Salam and Farid both go off for a day to see patients who live further away. I accompanied Salam to a village about twenty kilometres from Dhaka. I don't know how we found the right bus in the station, but we did. All of the buses, of which there were hundreds, looked identical and as equally decrepit not to mention badly parked. Apparently the destination was printed on the front so we just meandered past each bus until Salam recognised the town name. Once he had done so, Salam established that it was not going to leave for some time, but the driver could not be more specific. Not daring to wander far we sat on the steps drinking tea. I had managed to buy a cup with no condensed milk or sugar, the very thought of it made Salam shiver.

Half an hour later the bus was timetabled to leave, but the driver had disappeared. The small boys clinging to the outside trying to flog bits of plastic junk to us did not try to hurry him when he eventually arrived, none the less we did slowly rattle off. The boys persevered for a few miles before they hopped down at a traffic light that in a fit of madness the driver had decided to stop at!

We were very excited when we passed the centre's sign standing boldly on an empty piece of land - the land Valerie was trying to buy. I could tell from the look on Salam's face that he was thinking the same thoughts as me, hoping that the plot of land would not be empty for too much longer and that the sign would soon be advertising the new centre.

Salam set a price and we were off on a rickety rickshaw, one that was narrower than most...or was it the combination of two large bottoms that just made it seem narrower? Two hours later I was feeling very sorry for myself. The journey was scenic and blissfully quiet, though it seemed unending. But my discomfort can't have compared to that of the rickshaw boy, who was only a few inches wide.

We were deposited outside a row of huts built on stilts on the bank. The first one was a tea shop and this was our destination. I could not tell that the tea seller was disabled because he was sitting down surrounded by playing children and chatting to his caring wife. He was doing well both financially and medically. I was not so lucky with my cup of tea though this time. Our patient made us a cup in the standard way which I knew I had to swallow in order not to offend him. My teeth curled as I watched him pour a thimble full of tea into the tiny chipped cup, followed by a generous serving of the condensed milk and heaps of sugar.

I had drunk such tea before in the centre's own tea shop. The purpose of the tea shop is to train patients to run a shop, which was exactly how our host learnt his trade. In the centre patients buy a cup of the tiny, strong, sweet tea for the equivalent of a penny. Our home visit turned out to be more of a social visit as he was doing so well and needed no advice or help. His tea shop, I was told, brought in 200 Taka a day (£4), which was a good income.

Our second visit was not so encouraging. We went to see an old man who had regressed since the last home visit. He was lying in the dust on the ground, and looked no more than a heap of bones covered with wrinkled skin. He was anaemic and malnourished, and even his grandchildren had no energy to play because they were so thin and riddled with disease. Our ex-patient had had to sell off his shop to pay for his daughter's wedding and had since given up on life. Salam grew quite angry and assertively explained that the centre would give him a loan to re-start his shop, but only if he promised to pick up his life again.

During the four hour journey home I asked Salam why he had not re-admitted the man. Salam said it would not have helped because it is what the patient expected and hoped to hear and it was better for the patient to fend for himself. If he returned to the centre he would be fed up and sent home only to deteriorate again, but if he worked to set up a shop it would spark off the desire to live and to make something of himself. I never did hear the outcome of that story. As I listened I became aware of a greasy wet feeling on my legs. I was propped up against a Hessian sack of butter and it was not a cool day!

Salam seemed determined to get me to try some of his paan - chopped betel nut and lime rolled up in a paan leaf. Salam chews it all day, as do millions of others in the region. In many poor families the wife prepares whatever food she has and feeds the men in the family first, then the children which often means that there are no left-overs for herself so she will eat paan. Paan is an appetite suppressor, but also causes cancer of the tongue and throat. The number of throat cancer cases is higher in South East Asia than in the rest of the world due to paan and more females die of it than men. The betel nut leaves a dark residue on the consumer's teeth and makes saliva red, hence the red spit marks everywhere. When I had declined Salam's offer once, he bought me sweets every time we made subsequent paan stops.

Salam and I made a brief visit to an ex-patient who had a real success story, one of which the centre is proud. Ashraf was a victim of polio as a child and had been a beggar for his family, his lame leg utilised to reach the hearts of passers-by. Ashraf was finally one of the cases to be admitted to the centre for rehabilitation in 1983. He worked hard at his exercises and was taught how to clean shoes. On any day of the week Abdul could be found outside the Shemolly cinema cleaning shoes from his low-level trolley, and had since saved enough to buy a house from his daily takings of thirty to fifty Taka. He went on to marry his wife from his wheelchair and had two children. The family intend to return to Ashraf's village and open a shop.

It is a Bengali custom always to serve something to a visitor, which is usually tea with condensed milk and sugar, a biscuit, and a full glass of water. There seemed to be a standard order of consumption of these refreshments. First the biscuit is eaten, then the water is drunk before taking the tea. Abdul bought us a cup of tea from a nearby stall. I wanted to pay for it, but Salam pointed out that serving food is part of the host's fulfilment of social obligations and is vital for maintaining their self-esteem. Therefore it was important not to deny your host the opportunity to give you food, however poor they may be.

On one occasion this custom caused me to feel guilty because my hostess fed me on chicken and I knew it was the only meat that her family would have to eat in the whole week. I was constantly touched by the Bengalis' hospitality and the way in which they shared what little they had. Of course, there were also the people who only wanted money from me, but I became hardened and never gave any money to beggars, even if they were young or had no limbs. I had even heard stories from other aid workers who had given money near where they lived and were hassled every evening from then on. One woman I met decided only to give money to females and children and another man said he refused to give to people calling on Allah. I admired one volunteer who bought fruit and bread for the beggars, which ensured that they ate nutritious things rather than spending the money on cigarettes. At least the homeless do not spend their money on drink like so many in London because Bangladesh is a dry country with no off-licences or pubs. Spirits and wines are made in the homes of some who are not practising Muslims and a few shops sell alcohol in the non Muslim communities.

I was shocked to learn that all of the grossly disfigured people who lay on farmgate bridge were owned by a 'pimp'. The rich 'owner' of these people deposited them in the morning and then collected them and their begging bowls in the evening. The pimp keeps the money in exchange for providing the maimed people with a shelter and a minimal amount of food.

People are constantly asking me if the Bengalis are a nice race, and I always find the question hard to answer. Within the centre I do not believe there was a character who was not extremely caring and kind or anyone who I could not get along with. Yet, as in any big city, many people whom I encountered on the streets were rude and harsh. The centre had an unique atmosphere, almost one of a family and all of the Bengalis who I specialised with were also kind and fun to be with. So in answering the question I reply 'yes', but I can never ignore the memories of incidents in the shops and on the local transport.

Chapter 17

The Gold of Bangladesh

I only once travelled any distance independently of the centre. Tim, who sometimes helped out at sport time (when he was not coaching the Bengali cricket team), knew the owner of a tea estate in Kulara near the Shylet, which is where the vast majority of Bengali immigrants in England come from. He arranged a long weekend for us in the tea estate. Swarup and Holly came with us and thanks to our interpreter we travelled on an overnight train in great comfort and were picked up in the morning in the Land Rover belonging to the Manna tea plantation. We were welcomed at the house, which stood on stilts, with a breakfast consisting of parota, fried egg and curried chicken. There were only ourselves and the housekeeper in the house because the owners were in the East End of London where they are now residents.

We spent two glorious days roaming through the paddy fields and tea plantations. It was so quiet and generally when people saw us they stayed away - which made a pleasant change to the crowds in Dhaka. We joined in on a game of football being played in a dried paddy field and drunk tea in the small cluster of huts where the workers lived. I went for a walk on my own with only goats, cows and vivid yellow butterflies for company. It was bliss after two months of constant company. I sat in a bamboo wood and listened to the birds and insects and the occasional laughing child.

Apart from the hill tracts, the tea-growing area surrounding Shylet is the hilliest district in the country. It is supposed to have the best climate of the country too, with cool temperatures in winter rising only to fairly warm in the summer. However, we experienced heavy rain and spectacular electrical storms which plundered our house into darkness. We later found out that the area also has the highest annual rainfall and that just across the border in India was Cherrapury, the wettest place on Earth.

The storm shook the house that night and the noise coupled with the ghost stories we insisted on telling each other prevented us from sleeping. In the morning the sun shone warmly enough to tempt us back out into the muddy fields to roam the tea estate. We met one of the directors who told us that the Manna tea plantation covers 450 acres and at picking time employs 9000 people, mostly women. It must be a colourful sight with so many bending women in bright saris. Tea is Bangladesh's second largest export and hence a source of foreign income (manpower exports to the Middle East are the largest) with thirty thousand tons of tea being produced annually from the thousands of acres of tea gardens.

We were in Kulara on the Language Martyr's Day (21st February). In 1952 some Bengali students opposed the government's attempts to deny the Bengali language the status of State Language. Their cause was successful, but several lives were lost. The martyrs are remembered each year and in Dhaka thousands of people attend a special function held at the Central Shaheed Minar, the martyrs' monument. The people in the village of the Manna tea estate constructed their own mini monument and celebrated well into the night, making music that resembled the drone of bees and spoiling the peace of the countryside.

Swarup and I set off for the town hunting for crisps and soft drinks, for which we were suddenly all gasping. We felt virtuous after our five mile walk, and could see for miles across the paddy fields and the pockets of people carrying out their daily lives. Men ran past us with bundles of jute, which is used to make baskets, strapped to their backs. The west does not value this natural and biodegradable fibre so the farmer does not end up making much from the crop, but in Bangladesh it is considered to be the gold of the country.

The town of Kulara had one main street with market stalls selling everything from plastic buckets to saris and lunghis. I was interested in buying a sari so that I could use the cloth to decorate my room in the nurses' home. It was five and a half yards long, and would probably have run the length of all four walls in a room in a hall of residence. I couldn't find any material I liked, so I ended up buying two metres of chequered cloth that was meant for a lunghi.

Our bags of coke, cloth and crisps were too heavy to carry all of the way back so Swarup negotiated with a cycle rickshaw boy to take us the three miles across the paddy fields along the raised flood banks. It was dusk and we were guided home by a beautiful sunset. We could see little clusters of lights where people were eating their evening meals at home and it made me laugh that Swarup and I had gone to such great lengths, admittedly enjoyable ones, to buy fizzy drinks which in Dhaka we so easily grew sick of. I think we must have been addicted to the sugar after relying on bottles of fizz to quench our thirst at the centre - I had developed a sweet tooth like most Bengalis.

We were served delicious food three times a day at the tea estate, but each meal was exactly the same. The chicken curry was exquisite and made a pleasant change from Lilsa (the standard variety of fish) curry that I ate in Dhaka. There are three main forms of rice dishes served in Bangladesh. Biryani rice with chicken or beef, Pulao, spiced like biryani, but with no meat and baht, which is plain rice. Chicken tikka and kebabs are two common dishes which are usually served with nan bread or rice prepared in butter. In the poorer villages the diet consists of mainly rice, vegetables, dahl and chappatis with lots of chillies.

We returned to Dhaka feeling well rested even after a day's journey in a third class carriage sitting on hard wooden benches. We opted for the bottom so that we could see what it was like. The advantage of our relative discomfort was that we saw the sights from the windows. At each station our window was blocked by inquisitive faces and beggars who knocked on the glass hoping that we would pass some money through. They usually went straight to the first class windows despite the carriages normally being fairly empty, but it did not take long for the word to get around that there were some Badeshis in the third class compartment. Sellers poured in through the doors to tempt us with their refreshments - we shared a refreshing young coconut that had a hole cut in the top so that we could sip the sweet milk from inside with straws. Each station had several 'fast-food' stalls selling samosas, luchis (a crusty fried vegetable), puri (somewhat like tortilla) and aloe, which is a vegetable 'chop'. The smells were tempting, but we were nervous of eating the food even though with such a fast turnover it was probably safe because it was always kept hot.

The scenery did not vary to any great degree, with low-lying fields spreading as far as the eye could see, interrupted by small hills where mud huts were built above the water line. Along one stretch of the railway were posts with white paint marks indicating where the last floods had reached. It was a terrifying thought because I could see that many of the villages were not built above the flood mark, as I already knew to be the case from the news bulletins in Britain.

During some of the long lunch breaks at the centre Holly and I went sightseeing. We had to restrict our visits to one a week because unfortunately there were not many buildings of interest, mainly because the country never had the money to build anything to last or of any grandeur. Before I went to Bangladesh I heard that Dhaka was a city of seven hundred mosques and my mind boggled with images of Istanbul. In fact, most of the mosques were hideous concrete constructions, though the Istara Mosque and Kashaifully Mosque were worth a visit. Being female we were not allowed inside, but from the outside we could appreciate the exquisite architecture of the Moghul period (1576 to 1757).

Our visit also coincided with one of the five prayers of the day. The Muezin calls the followers of the Muslim faith to prayer, starting at five in the morning (which I eventually learnt to sleep through). As we stood admiring the architecture of the mosque our view became blocked by thousands of bottoms. The worshippers were all kneeling facing Mecca with their bottoms raised so that they could kiss the ground. It was a funny sight - row upon row of rear ends clad in white trousers.

We also saw the Ahsan Manzil, which was the palace of the last Nawab of Dhaka, though now in a state of disrepair. Until the previous year the beautiful pink palace had been taken over by the homeless who, after many years of inhabitance, were slowly ruining the building. The Bengali government recognised the importance of maintaining their heritage and ordered everyone out and made plans for renovation.

The most impressive building I saw was the Lalbagh Fort, built in 1678. Its picture is stamped on the 10 Taka notes and is the pride of the city.

Swarup took Holly and me to the Balda gardens, which has a

sizable collection of rare flowers. It was a haven of quietness which we were enjoying until a Bengali family asked me to pose with them and for Holly to take the picture. Swarup advised us not to because we would only be used to show off to friends of the family when the pictures were put in the family album. It is very prestigious to have photographs of white people and they were keen not to miss their chance. In the end Holly and I gave in to their pestering just to be rid of them, making sure my smile in the photo was noticeably fake. It was not to be the last time we were asked and some men went as far as to pose draped around us.

At the centre I took a number of photos of the patients who I initially believed had no such thing as a photograph of themselves. I soon caught on that many others before me had been under the same impression and consequently the people who had been patients for a while had personal albums full of their own pictures.

I spent one infuriating day trying to get a telephone line to England to phone a friend, but was told that I would have to wait for anything up to six hours. I could not sit by the office phone for so long and it was impossible to ring direct onto an international line. I resorted to trying the Sheraton Hotel, who managed to get me a line within ten minutes. I then put them to the test and asked for a Bulgarian line to say happy birthday to my father. They succeeded in just a quarter of an hour and I think Dad was as amazed to hear from me as I was to be speaking to him. Bengali post is unreliable, but I risked it with a few postcards. However, there was an excellent safeguard system of giving letters to departing aid workers. Anyone flying straight home sent the word out and fully expected to play postman. Luckily letters arrived safe and sound each time at the GPO address, so I never felt homesick. I was nicknamed the Chiti girl by Khokon because I received so many letters. One day when he gave me eight he pleaded that I should stay so that he remained in his job!

Chapter 18

Joyti and Poppy

Saturdays were put aside for non emergency admittances. Patients queued up outside to await their turn in being examined by each member of the team. The physiotherapist and nurse checked the medical side and the social worker went into their financial position. If the team did not feel it was necessary to admit the person they were usually given an out patients appointment. For those who had travelled miles to see the specialists and could not make a weekly appointment an immediate assessment was made so that some simple movements could be demonstrated to them straight away to do at home.

Twice a week the outpatients' clinic was held in the physiotherapy hut at the centre. Hosneara examined the females and Roman checked over the men and when I was there a Canadian physiotherapist, who specialised in children, was holding her own clinic. The physiotherapists ultimate aim was to make each patient feel part of the team so that they would learn quickly and be able to take responsibility for themselves back at home. This aim was not restricted to out patients. Before the appointments were terminated any aid needed was measured for and made in the workshops.

Two adorable boys came from the Mother Theresa's home across the road. On two occasions I went to collect the boys, who sat on one hip each and loved the journey. They imitated horns and all of the noises that scream out twenty-four hours a day on the Farmgate road.

Three other regular children made a morning's journey from Sreepur with an English aid worker. They were orphan children, from the Families for Children project, sponsored by British Airways. I visited the orphanage at Sreepur and found that it houses six hundred children from just a few months old to teenagers. Once the children are accepted the village takes care of all their needs, including health and education. In the playing room I saw one of the centre-made rocking chairs being put to good use. It was good to see it withstanding a tough life.

While the patients were waiting their turn in the outpatients' clinic the men set up a game of Caram, which is played everywhere. It is rather like mini-snooker, except that the thumb is used instead of a cue and discs replace the balls. I joined in on a few games, but never really mastered the art. A patient who I nicknamed Mr Lazy played it in every spare minute of the day and more. He used to be found leading other patients astray playing during his allocated time in the occupational therapy unit. If it had been a professional game I am sure Mr Lazy would have been a very rich man. Another favourite was challenging me to an arm wrestle. Any patient who has been in a wheelchair for any length of time is a tough challenge because their arms become their legs and are generally very strong - as I found out to my disadvantage. For those weaker people it was an excellent fun way to exercise.

Valerie was very keen for her volunteers to see other projects and arranged visits for us to a home for deaf children and a rehabilitation centre for destitute women, both run by the government. The centre for destitute women was particularly interesting - they took in young girls who had got pregnant out of marriage, a grave sin in the Muslim religion. During their pregnancy the mothers learn to weave and sew and are taught basic health education. After the birth they breast-feed for three months and then must leave without their child. The centre finds homes for the children (they found a home for Poppy with Valerie) and has the satisfaction of knowing that they have protected the young girls from having an illegal abortion. Many girls manage to have their child without their family ever finding out, though they will never be able to have a family of their own because they are no longer virgins.

The other project we visited was the nutrition centre run by Save The Children. Their hospital was like any in the UK. They provide ante-natal immunisation, family planning and TB clinics on an outpatient basis and see some two hundred children and mothers daily. They also have sixty beds for severely malnourished children. A doctor told us some spine curling facts: seven per cent of Bengali women marry at ten years old and ninety per cent are married by sixteen.

It was always fun to be asked to look after Valerie's two children, Joyti and Poppy. I was more involved with Poppy because her sister went to school every day, though I sometimes went to collect Joyti after her classes which was amusing as it gave me a taste of the bossy side of her character. On her frame Joyti would barge her way through the crowded streets on the walk home and stand no nonsense if people didn't move in time. She used her frame as a weapon and hit the ankles of offenders, which resulted in a fast journey home.

Poppy loved having stories read to her and during my stay her favourite was the Gingerbread Man. She especially liked being read to when she was strapped to the tilting table which was used in Poppy's case to encourage her to take her weight through her legs. Poppy cannot stand alone, but being strapped to the tilting table meant that her legs were kept in the correct position without letting her knees bend back as they did when she was just supported by an adult. The workshop made Poppy some callipers to prevent this from happening as she practised walking. A long term volunteer called Patience made Poppy a bean bag to play with and thus encourage control in her hands. It was only the size of her hand and soon she was asking for her 'handbag'.

Another messy activity was bathing Poppy. The Cerebral Palsy disease she suffers from causes Poppy's arms and right leg to move in spasms and she cannot make them do what she wants, which in this case was to keep still. Poppy did get clean, but so did the bathroom floor and my clothes. I grew very fond of the two girls who were so easy to play with and to talk to. They were spoilt by the volunteers, who all take a shine to them because they are so loving, such fun and their beautiful smiles are so rewarding.

One afternoon while everyone was getting ready to play sport I started to throw the ball to the patients in the yard. It developed into a popular pastime, especially for Mr Chairman and was also popular with the physiotherapists who saw that different muscles were being worked and balance improved. I thought I had invented a new kind of exercise until Holly told me that it was an old faithful!

Robbie asked me to draw up a new list of items for sale made in the two workshops. I was astonished to see a list of more than seventy items. I started by quoting prices of hand-woven bags, wooden toys, jewellry and educational games and then started a new column for wheelchairs, callipers, backbraces, walking sticks and frames. A few Australian volunteers had designed the toys, which explains why kangaroo and koala puzzles are made. Other designs were accumulated by looking through catalogues.

Shemoll had literally copied the designs of the centre's original wheelchairs and callipers from western prototypes. Valerie tried to explain how a striker bed works to Shemoll, but he found it impossible to design one with the correct measurements without actually seeing one of the beds. At first Valerie was pessimistic about finding such a specialised bed in Bangladesh, but after much searching she found the only one, in the military hospital. Shemoll went and took its measurements and now the centre has three striker beds of its own, all of which are in continuous use. The backbraces that are produced are made-to-measure and worn by patients who have migrated from bed rest, but still need support while new hard bone sets properly in the spine.

When I had finished my piece of artwork Robbie asked if I would like to go with him to deliver an order made to Aarong. We loaded up the tempo with boxes full of puzzles and swinging parrots and went to the craft shops' warehouse. The place was a shambles and we joined the long queues of people offering their handicrafts. After some hours we made it to the front. The unfriendly man sitting behind the desk made us undo each bag so that he could take out each individual toy to inspect it. Sixty swinging parrots and eighty puzzles later he was satisfied. He then proceeded to fill out a mountain of official forms, most of which were copies done without carbon paper. The process made me think back to when I had applied for my visa in London and had to fill in three identical forms separately. The delivery of our goods took up the entire afternoon and was a good example of office inefficiency.

If ever there was a craft fair Valerie sent some of the patients along to the centre's stall and she sometimes took people to the two craft shops in Dhaka, Aarong and Kumudini, which were geared for tourists and charged accordingly. I couldn't work out why any patients would want to see an expensive shop even if it stocked a few of the toys made by the centre. Valerie explained that half of the patients had never had a toy in their life and could not see why they had to spend hours making these luxuries when they didn't really know what they were for. By showing them the shops they could begin to understand the world of luxury and knew that their manpower would be appreciated by the elite few who had money to spend on non-essential things.

There was a small display cabinet in the centre which every visitor is encouraged to look at and hopefully to buy from. The ex-patriot community tended to be good customers, especially the British who had more to do with the centre. People sometimes put in orders for a specific toy to be made for a Christmas present or asked for a beloved broken toy to be copied. The British community also helped Valerie's cause by holding an annual bazaar in aid of the centre. The crafts were also exported to Britain, Australia, United States, Canada and Japan. The money from the sales made the workshop self-sufficient. In a typical year nearly £4000 worth of craftwork was sold - by no means all profit, but in a healthy year the surplus would be spent on new tools or something that was needed to make the production line more efficient.

Robbie was very keen to promote the importance of occupational therapy, which so few people knew anything about - least of all the deprived Bangladeshis. He expressed how vital it was in increasing the confidence of a recently disabled person and in helping them to realise that there were still activities they could do. This included anything from transferring themselves to a chair or learning to cook and clean again to coping out in the fields with livestock or earning a living through selling fishing nets. However big or small the task, everything can seem impossible at first with a broken neck or back.

In mid-speech Robbie suddenly stopped telling me about the importance of keeping everyone busy and inquired as to whether he could call me 'Jute'. I was a little miffed at being likened to a plant that is made into rush matting, but agreed. The reason that Robbie thought of me as jute was because of my blonde hair. He had seen blondish or peroxided hair on other volunteers in the past, but claimed that he had never seen my hair before and that the only other thing he had seen which resembled the colour was drying jute. Thankfully the name never stuck, although when I thought of it in terms of the gold of Bangladesh instead of a plant that is sunk in water for months to rot before being dried, the name did not seem so bad.

A home made wheelchair
This photograph was taken in the outskirts of Dhaka.
The disabled man has not been fortunate enough to have
been a patient at the centre, and has had to make his own
wheelchair.

Chapter 19

Old Dhaka on a Motorbike

On a blisteringly hot day in March I went with Khokon on a series of errands. I readily agreed to accompany him to various hospitals and warehouses thinking that I would travel in style in the ambulance, but it was not to be. Instead I found myself on the back of a motorbike in a huge helmet. I would never mock the importance of a helmet especially as we made our journey just five days after Farid and Monica (the head nurse) were involved in a nasty accident. An oncoming vehicle had hit the motorbike and both of the riders were thrown off. Farid escaped with nothing more serious than grazes because he had been wearing a helmet, but Monica was less lucky. She had been riding side-saddle with no helmet, which is tragically how all females travel on motorbikes.

There is no actual reason why females don't wear helmets other than tradition and vanity. They ride side-saddle because it is thought indecent to straddle. The result of this for Monica was a badly-cut forehead and a suspected fractured skull. Both Farid and Monica were taken from the scene of the accident to a hospital. Farid didn't need attention and Monica requested to be cared for in the centre. A neurosurgeon examined Monica and was satisfied that nothing had been broken. She was fortunate only to be suffering from shock, cuts and bruises. My only objection to wearing a helmet was that it felt like I had stuck my head in a furnace.

We had to use the motorbike because our list of errands included buying rubber from Old Dhaka where the streets are too narrow for the ambulance. It was for that very reason that the centre bought four motorbikes from donated funds. Our first stop was at the Compath Laboratory, which was where all of the blood tests were analysed. It cost the centre about £1 per basic blood test each time a test tube of blood was sent there and this could increase by anything up to £6 for a more specialised test, while an X-ray cost £2 per film.

The centre had been donated a portable X-ray machine, but it could only cope with simple X-rays and any advanced pictures had to be taken at Compath. The prices sound low compared with Britain, but it is easy to forget that every penny is precious to the centre. The centre's own pathology lab did not have the equipment to carry out the tests on site, besides which the pathologist was only employed on a part-time basis. Fortunately Compath is a modern place, equipped with the latest technology.

We then ventured into Old Dhaka where there was always a frenzy of activity both on the water with all of the ferries and trading boats and also in the bazaars that were grouped according to type of merchandise. People moved like a colony of ants, darting in and out finding the best bargains. We slowly made our way through the Hindu section where I saw old men sitting on the floor holding shells between their feet which they attacked with a huge curved blade to make bracelets. Around the corner was a street that sold spices and here the aroma in the air clung to our clothes and hair. We passed dark alleyways lined with Hessian sacks: the sacks were people's homes and the place inevitably stank of urine.

The most colourful area was the fruit, veg and flower market. I asked Khokon to stop so that I could take a photograph of all the fresh fruit and veg piled high. The sight of pumpkins, sweet potatoes, cucumber, carrots, beans, watermelons, lichees, mangoes, guavas, bananas and oranges would have made my parents' mouths water after a winter in Bulgaria where the only available vegetables were peppers. There were also cauliflowers, turnips, beets, peas, lettuce, tomatoes and apples for sale during the winter and spring seasons, the two seasons that overlapped with my stay.

In Bangladesh there are six recognised seasons. Borsho is the monsoon which comes in June and stays until August and I purposefully missed this even though the countryside is at its richest and prettiest and the mangoes are at their most delicious stage. Mangoes are my favourite fruit and Bangladesh is known for its mangoes because they are the largest and sweetest in the world - one very good reason for spending three months there.

Autumn falls in mid-August through to mid-October, followed

by the dewy season (Hemento) which lasts until mid-December. I
arrived in winter and stayed through spring, until April. When I
complained about the heat to Khokon I received little comfort on
hearing that in summer the humidity rises to between 80 and 105
degrees Fahrenheit, day and night. I was shrivelling during the
supposedly cool months when the temperature remained around 75
degrees and the nights were cool.

Khokon came out of a shop with boxes piled high. He looked
funny trying to look over the top of them in order to see where he
was going. When I finally registered that they would have to be
strategically balanced on me to get back to the centre the smile
immediately dropped from my face. Sure enough, I had two boxes
on each knee, and one perched on top making a pyramid. This
meant that I had to sit quite far back and had no chance of holding
onto Khokon for support, though Khokon promised to go slowly
and not to slam on his brakes. To my amazement we made it back
in one piece with all the boxes intact.

I only had three weeks left in Bangladesh, the thought of which
made me sad and a touch alarmed because Valerie was about to go
for a month's holiday in England with the girls. I could not imagine
the centre without Valerie's daily work from as early as six in the
morning until long after everyone had gone home. It was not so
easy to get rid of her, either. The night before she was due to fly,
Valerie announced that she had too much work to do and could in
no way leave the next day. No words could persuade her to change
her mind, so in the morning I went to the British Airways office to
change her ticket. It was relatively painless despite having to re-
order two wheelchairs to be waiting for them at Heathrow and
having to explain that a special chair and walking frame would still
be going on board with them.

I admired Valerie for coping with the fourteen hour flight and
two cerebral palsy children all on her own. Their departure was
postponed for two days, when they finally left for a well-earned
rest. Valerie never really rests from the centre though, even when
on holiday, because she gives talks all around England to raise
awareness and finances for the centre. Every October she spends a
hectic month in the British Isles to promote her work. Her timetable

is amazing: a speech in Kent one day might be followed by another in Ireland the next.

I was surprised at how easy it was to change Valerie's ticket because any vaguely clerical procedure usually took three hours to complete. An incredible amount of forms have to be filled in for the slightest thing, all of which have to be signed by at least half a dozen people and you can be sure that all six will never be available at once. If you ever ask for a receipt you will be given three pieces of paper. My sister, who hoards receipts, would have had to exchange her already bulging wallet for a suitcase.

There was one activity that I still had not joined in with at the centre: school. Every morning from eight until ten Madhab held a reading and writing class, with a little bit of maths. Any patient who was illiterate and that included most of them, attended school as part of their rehabilitation programme. Madhab tried to teach everyone to sign their name and to master the alphabet so that they could understand signs. He also aimed to teach his pupils basic maths so that they could partake in the money world. Shopkeeping was the most successful form of training in the centre, so it was imperative that the prospective shopkeeper understood money. It was mind-boggling how few people from the remoter parts of the country knew about money: most of them grew their own food which they used in exchange for pottery, tools or materials. Therefore they had no need of money. Having a shop in a small village often does not bring in enough money to keep a family fed and clothed, so the patients are encouraged also to make paper bags or fishing nets to sell.

I tried to sit in on a lesson, but it was all conducted in Bengali and the text books were also written in the language, so I never grasped what was going on. Madhab just looked at me as though he had given up on me. But he was not the only teacher - the educated patients were prompted to help the uneducated ones. Bablu was a thirteen year old boy who needed no prompting. He had reached year six at school and was delighted to have such an opportunity to practice his English, his favourite subject. He had been stabbed in the back and neck by his neighbour for no known reason and his spinal cord was damaged to the extent that he would never walk again. When Bablu was told the terrible news he said that he felt no emotion and it was all Allah's work.

Bablu worked hard in the centre and consequently made good progress. He loved to help others too and one day I saw him teaching Jobeda how to use a tape-measure. She wanted to start up a business selling clothes she made herself, but never having been to school nor received a maths lesson in her life she did not understand inches or centimetres. Bablu wanted to set up his own cloth business and with his capabilities and enthusiasm I'm sure he'll do well. He was one of the few at the centre who were optimistic about their own future from the beginning. He couldn't wait to show his new wheelchair off to his friends and to demonstrate his newly-learnt tricks, such as the wheelie.

Bablu had a great advantage in that he was returning to his loving parents who owned a three roomed house built from brick and supplied with electricity and fans. His doting mother shared Bablu's first few months in the centre with him, sleeping on the floor under his bed and helping to relieve the pressure of work from the nursing staff by taking care of his daily needs in the centre at their sides. Others could not have their relatives with them, not even some unfortunate ones who lived their last days in the centre. Due to a combination of appalling communication systems and bad roads that made travelling difficult, some grieving relatives would arrive a couple of days after their loved one had passed away.

Chapter 20

Reflections

Holly was the last volunteer to arrive in my time at the centre, and the first to leave after just six weeks. We had become good friends during our month and a half of living and working together and I was sad to see her go. She had made a big impression having spent long hours working on patients and staff and using the osteopathic methods which were new to everyone. Holly was also remembered for her easy-going attitude and her singing. On her last day there was a mishti (the sweet cakes that all Bengalis seem to crave) party held in her honour, at which long speeches were made in both English and Bengali and songs were sung by Shotorbabu and Holly. They made a delightful duo when they sung 'Twinkle Twinkle Little Star' and I'm sure I wasn't the only one to be left with a lump in my throat.

Wendy's departure two weeks later was no less impressive, with speeches made by Wendy in Bengali and a feast laid on for everyone to supplement the mishti. Mishti parties are held on any special occasion. Ward one became quiet again and even Khokon lost his appetite for Connect Four for a while.

With such a short time left myself I started to dwell on things. I certainly had not saved the world like I had knowingly unrealistically dreamt of doing at school, but I did feel that I had helped ease the life of some of the centre's patients and staff. Admittedly the beginning had been a little tough, although it could have been a lot worse had my blues lasted more than a couple of days, if it were not for the prompt cure of which I am grateful to Theresa. I had made some good English friends who I knew I would keep in contact with, but what was more important was the value of my numerous Bengali friends. I felt I had learnt about a new culture and also had the opportunity to become part of a special community for a short time. I also came up with a theory that I know I am not alone in thinking, which is that remembering to listen, question and learn is the most important thing for any volunteer in the Third World. We must not assume we know better. I also believe that any new ideas and determination to improve things must be combined with humility and politeness.

Prior to going to the Centre for the Rehabilitation of the Paralysed I thought that most aid work had religious connections to it and being an atheist I always felt dubious about partaking in any project. For me, the excellent thing about the centre was the way in which all religions were respected and encouraged. Valerie is a Christian and her strong faith is obviously very important to her, but she is a very private Christian and never forces her beliefs on anyone. Whilst I was at the centre several Muslim festivals and two Hindu festivals were celebrated.

When I attended one of Valerie's talks in London I was introduced to a lady who said I was very brave to go out as a volunteer at such a young age. She then went on to say how she wished she had done something similar, but she had not been a Christian in her teens. When I replied that neither was I she seemed astounded, but this was the general response I received whilst out in Bangladesh too. There were very few people who were not working under the eye of God, but I want to stress that being a minority was by no means a disadvantage and did not affect my stay in any way. It quickly became apparent that I was the youngest volunteer by about five years, but I never felt it mattered. In the same way John Wilkins, a fellow volunteer who introduced me to the Charles family, never let the fact that back at home he would be classed as an old age pensioner stop him from enjoying himself at the centre in the metal workshop. He had been a postman in his Devon village, but since retiring has visited the centre on an annual basis. To us, age meant nothing, but I was quite pleased to be among company of my own age after I had left.

Even when Valerie had gone on holiday with her two girls her presence still seemed strong. Valerie's determination and patience will never cease to amaze me. She never forgets a face or a name and on meeting an ex-volunteer she can always come up with a story about them no matter how long ago their visit to the centre may have been.

In my last few days there I was delighted to see Shotorbabu walking short distances at a time on his own and to be able to watch

Fozzil confidently complete a puzzle using his right arm and hand. I no longer had to feel quite so bad at deserting my fruit-feeding duties because Mr Bimalendu had mastered the art himself. Abdus B. Salam was preparing to go home himself to live with his mother. I could not forget the five unfortunate people who did not make it, but on the whole my memories of patients are positive and happy ones.

I had to go home with souvenirs for my family, so I spent my last lunch hour in Kumuadmi where I purchased some beautiful cushion covers embroidered in the traditional style, called nokshicanta. Scenes from everyday life were captured by the stitches in every colour of the rainbow. The other souvenirs on offer included jewellry, brasswork, leatherwork, ceramics, jute products, woodcarvings and pottery. The unique items that were beyond my budget were pink pearls, fine muslin and jamdaur or silk saris. None of the craftsmanship was expensive in relation to the high quality. A friend kindly bought me a pink pearl to take home for myself.

When April 12th inevitably arrived I could not believe that I had been at the centre for three months, though my diary confirmed it. The time had sped by as if it had only been three weeks, though in other ways I felt like I had been there a lifetime because I had been made to feel so at home.

I knew I couldn't make a speech in Bengali, especially not one to match Wendy's or Holly's. People knew me for my supposed art work and posters, so I decided to make a huge card to leave behind along with my money thermometer and other posters. A friend helped me to draw a colourful picture, then I asked Swarup to translate my message. I had the fun task of copying out the Bengali script, which to me looked like lines and scribbles. My marking must have made some sense because Rhaman was able to read it out to the gathering of patients and staff on my last morning. It read,

Thank you very much for making me feel so at home here in the centre. I have enjoyed my brief visit enormously and will take home lots of fond memories. I shall be thinking of you all during the great move and look forward to seeing you all happily settled in the new dream centre.

It went down well and Hosneara, Rhaman, Madhab and Mr

Lazy all made very touching speeches. Shotorbabu sung as the infamous mishti were handed around. Looking around the gathering of patients I noticed several new faces and also many familiar faces of those who had been at the centre throughout my time. I looked warmly at Abdus B Salam who was standing at the back. The only visible sign of any disability was his neck collar. I then had great visions of him one day being an ordinary able-bodied man living happily in his village, though since then he has written to me with the news that he still feels pain in his neck and waist. I was touched to receive a letter from Salam as he had taken a lot of time and trouble to write to me in English - a commendable accomplishment considering he only attended school for three years.

Not being able to find certain faces, such as Chairman's, was a good thing because it meant that they were back at home rebuilding their lives with their families.

As I listened to Shotorbabu sing I knew he too would soon be going home to his wife and daughters. Since his discharge he has resumed his singing lessons. I would never have thought in my wildest dreams that Fozzil would be walking through his village to his tea-shop where he now works to keep his wife and son, making more money than he did as a labourer. Mr Bimalendu is currently at home doing what he does best which is lecture science in the university. Soon after I left he progressed into a wheelchair and was able to go downstairs to help Madhab teach the non educated patients which I believe he enjoyed greatly.

I could not postpone the moment any longer if I wanted to be in my booked seat on the flight to India, so I got a babytaxi and jumped in before anyone saw the tears pouring down my cheeks.

On the way to the airport I recalled a question people asked me thousands of times before my visit which was 'Why Bangladesh?' At the time my only answer was that I was lucky to have found work anywhere, but now it is 'Why not?' There are millions of fabulous reasons for going to Bangladesh, the centre aside. The people, culture, scenery and lack of tourists are to mention but a few.

There have been many ways and opportunities to keep in touch with the centre and the people involved, all of which I have welcomed as I would never want to let any of it fade away into the past. I receive a newsletter regularly, which informs me of the latest developments and I have many fiends who write to me, the most dear being Swarup and Valerie. Holly, Wendy and I have managed to keep in touch and thanks to a wonderful ex-long-term helper called Patience everyone manages to catch a glimpse of Valerie annually when she comes to England to do a publicity stint. Each year Patience holds a buffet lunch where it is possible to meet all the legendary names like Peter Hunt who is the man behind all of the publicity in the UK.

By sheer chance I have also been the lucky neighbour of Hosneara who has been in London for a year on a British Council award studying at the Institute of Child Health. She gained a diploma in Community Based Rehabilitation and I was pleased to be able to go to her graduation ceremony and watch the first Bengali to receive such a certificate. The centre is trying to encourage each patient to become health workers in their own right when they are discharged and return to their villages. Now Hosneara will be able to further the teaching in community based rehabilitation in her own country.

I learnt an amazing amount about the centre just before I gave a speech at my old school. I did a fair bit of research into the history of Valerie's centre and found many newspaper clippings and amusing stories about it. In April I had two weeks of annual leave from nursing and booked a flight on Gulf Air to Dhaka. Two days later war was declared in the Gulf and I was advised to give my trip a miss. I was extremely put out so I decided to raise some money for them instead.

Jenny and Rod, two very dear friends from nursing, said they would like to join me in a marathon walk through London. We chose to walk the same route as the London marathon and both Jenny and Rod completed it, but I had to wimp out half way with swollen and blistered feet. Nevertheless we raised £750.

Whilst on holiday in the summer of '91 I met some old friends who had started their own publishing company, Summersdale. I had already read the books they had written on busking and cookery when they asked me to do a book on my experiences in Dhaka. At first I laughed at the very idea of it and thought Stewart mad to even think up such an absurd plan. Later on however, I thought if they can do it, so can I. I took on the challenge and it turned out to be a fun and cheap way of occupying my evenings after a day's work in Next, which has paid for my ticket back to Bangladesh.

Chapter 21

The Future

There is a new and exciting future for the centre, which is now situated in a new site in Savaar, twenty kilometres from Dhaka. Savaar is frequently visited by tourists and Bengalis because it contains Bangladesh's national monument and is therefore accessed by a good road. The plot of land is about half a mile from the road and measures seven acres in total.

Buying land in Bangladesh is always stressful. For example, the plot of the land the centre purchased was once divided into three separate plots and the ownership of two of them had been disputed in the courts for ten years before the rightful owners were agreed on. The lease for the building in Farmgate ran out in March 1990, but at that stage Valerie was still battling to buy the land in Savaar. On April 4th the centre's future took a turn for the better when the land deeds were signed. I was lucky enough to go along and photograph this historic occasion. The Centre for the Rehabilitation of the Paralysed now had its own home for the first time.

In June sixty patients and the contents of the centre were transported to the temporary buildings on the new site. At first problems cropped up, one of them being that the toilets had to be rebuilt because they had been facing Mecca. At the moment there are temporary male and female wards, physiotherapy and occupational therapy departments, metal and wood workshops, an administration block, a recreational area and staff quarters. A basketball court has been built from funds provided by the British Film Industry and a vegetable plot has been sewn. The centre is now self-sufficient in rice and vegetables and also manages to sell their surplus produce in the local market. Four cows provide milk for the centre, as do the two goats. A pond has been dug and filled with fish, which are also eaten and sold, though there have been teething troubles with the pond as it evaporated in the dry season and flooded during the monsoon.

The land itself cost £105,000 to buy even though when the centre first moved in it was totally undeveloped apart from one tube well and a hand pump. It has been estimated that it will cost half a million pounds to develop the new purpose-built centre and that's after saving on more than half the cost of the temporary buildings by salvaging fixed appliances and other parts.

The plans for the permanent centre are magnificent and will include a small operating theatre, morgue, lecture room, prayer hall and beds for one hundred and twenty patients. There will be twelve private beds, which ultimately goes against Valerie's beliefs that everyone should receive the same treatment, but the Board of Trustees pointed out to Val that rich patients would otherwise pay to be treated in Bangkok unless they believed they would receive the same care at home and it would be a useful way of generating money. As well as this new income a bank has agreed to rent space in the centre for a branch.

The centre will have a half-way hostel for fifteen people who can take care of their own daily needs, but who are not yet ready to leave behind the security of the centre altogether. The staff accommodation will include twenty-four bachelor rooms and eighteen family homes.

Valerie is working on starting a school for cerebral palsy children in the local area and there will be eight beds for the mother and childcare project. This will enable a mother to join her child to learn the next stage in the child's care before returning to their village. A specially trained British teacher has already spent time in the centre helping to get the ball rolling.

Begum Raushan Ershad, the wife of the deposed dictator, has been a keen supporter of Val's work for many years and in May 1990 laid the foundation stone. The First Lady wrote the following message in the visitor's book,

"In the history of service to mankind your work will last forever. My best wishes will be with you."

She has given more than her best wishes, though. Begum Ershad donated one third of an acre of the land in Dhaka to the centre. At the moment the usual problems are being experienced and it is unclear who legally owns the land. If the centre comes out of the mess as the owner then it will be used as an office and as a small ward for critically ill people who need specialised hospital treatment.

Some other Bengali officials have also been very generous in providing a gas pipe and three phase power at no cost. The £16,000 stamp duty on the land purchase was also allowed to be ignored. The ministry of land sold a five acre plot of land fifteen miles from Dhaka to Valerie at a reduced cost. She hopes to use this area for income generation and employment creation projects for paralysed people, for example she intends to open a factory which will manufacture wheelchairs and walking aids. Two members of staff recently attended a course in food processing and were taught how to make jams, pickles, yoghurt, cakes and jellies. They are now in a position to teach some patients how to preserve food which they can then sell in their home communities.

The wheelchair workshop is now producing five chairs a week with two full-time staff. The Motivation team held an open day at the centre and had a promotion at the British Council to publicise the new chair to other projects, which immediately resulted in a small project ordering twenty-five wheelchairs and fifty pairs of crutches to be used in the area hit by the devastating cyclone in 1991.

Theresa has been working hard to teach patients basic health and hygiene through flip charts and eventually wants to send everyone home with a teaching aid pack so that they can pass on the information to their neighbours. They will also be taught how to treat scabies and other common diseases and will become basic health workers in their own community. This means that the centre is now doing much more than just helping the disabled population of Bangladesh. Valerie hopes to encourage patients to stick together and campaign for better facilities in their local towns for the disabled. A computer is also being installed to link up the centre with other similar centres for the disabled around the world.

To develop all three areas is going to cost one and a half million pounds and it is already costing £4,000 a month to run the centre. I hope that by writing this book I have given the reader a glimpse into Valerie Taylor's amazing work. I feel very lucky to have been able to experience it for myself and to have helped out in my own small way. If, having read this, you are moved by what Valerie is striving to achieve, please tell your friends about this book. You have already helped by buying this book, since all royalties from sales will be donated to the centre and for that I am very grateful, for the dream of Valerie and the disabled people of Bangladesh does not come cheaply. If you would like to make a direct donation please send cheques, made payable to Friends of the Centre for the Rehabilitation of the Paralysed (FCRP), charity number 328425, and send it to:

Mr Richard Fagan
The Appeal Secretary
The Church Office
St James Church
Oxford Road
Gerrards Cross
Buckinghamshire SL9 7DJ

All donations will be personally acknowledged. Please help us to realise our dream.

Epilogue

"I wish you will give your hands to the CRP again."
- From a card given to the author after the swim.

As soon as I realised that I had an opportunity to return to the Centre for the Rehabilitation of the Paralysed I leapt at the chance. I arranged my three month stay before even considering the implications. I thought that on the one hand it would be easier returning as I would know some of the people and have a reasonable idea of what would be expected of me, but on the other hand I realised that so many aspects of the centre would be different that my second visit would be a totally new experience.

The journey out to Bangladesh was as colourful as the first time and the delays were nearly as long. I arrived in the middle of the night, but was not remotely surprised to see Valerie waiting for me. I felt terribly guilty when she told me that she and Khokon had been at the airport on and off for ten hours. It was decided that it was too late to make the twenty kilometre trip out to Savaar so Khokon gallantly put us up for the remainder of the night. His family vacated the double bed so that Valerie and I could share it and I fell asleep to the musical sounds of six snorers. My first night had been a wonderful re-introduction to Bangladeshi life.

Slightly refreshed from the rigours of my journey, we completed the last lap early in the morning. I was able to watch the sunrise over the paddy fields and the smoking chimneys of the brick factories. As we left the carbon monoxide-filled air of Dhaka and headed north west into the country past waking markets I began to feel both excited and apprehensive as to what I would find at the new centre. When I saw the CRP sign and felt the bumpy track I suddenly wished that Holly and Wendy could be with me as we had all been talking about and waiting for this moment for the two years since we had reunited in England.

I find it hard to express in words how I felt when I got out of the smart new jeep donated by FCRP. I did not have time to take in my surroundings before I was swamped by the staff who had all gathered around the tea hut before their day's work started. Their smiles and welcoming words put me at ease and I was naturally touched that they had all remembered me and the things that I had contributed two years previously. My heart really swelled when the staff with whom I had little to do and a handful of patients came up to greet me, remembering me for my swim. I felt special knowing how many visitors and volunteers pass through the centre in one month, let alone two years. Two days later I was to be introduced at the patients' meeting as the swimmer, walker and author...I almost wished that I had a clean slate and didn't have all this to live up to.

From where I stood I took my first proper look at my surroundings. It was hard to believe that the last time I had trod the same ground it had been a muddy undeveloped field. The area was surrounded by a boundary wall, and was much bigger than I had remembered, though there was less in it than I had anticipated. The brick buildings had tin roofs and were equipped with all of the essential services, giving the impression of permanence, even though they were only temporary. Due to our early arrival the patients were still in bed, so there was little activity. Later, when the centre was in full swing, it did not have such a large air about it.

I made my way up to the office block along a path bordered with roses, and was greeted by Mohua with a cup of tea. Nothing had changed.

I was introduced to a new member of staff who works alongside Mohua, called Habib. On the verandah I tried to explain why I had given up nursing, but I don't think that anyone could fully comprehend that it is possible to give up a training for the purely selfish reason of not enjoying it.

A tour of the centre soon followed. It was both familiar and strange at once. The basic ideas behind the running of the centre all seemed the same, but their execution was different. The atmosphere also felt alien, but that was more to do with the new faces than with the new centre. In time I felt the same sensation of belonging, although the sheer size of the centre made it harder to be one big happy family.

My biggest shock came when I entered the temporary male ward. There is only one of these, with thirty-three beds crammed into it and more spilling out onto the verandah. The familiar smell made my stomach churn more than usual because here it was so intense. There was no sense of atmosphere. It may seem a harsh statement, but with everyone thrown together the patients seem more institutionalised. In the evenings when the television is on there is a bit more of a group feeling and on Wednesday evenings when 'Mr McGyver' is on, the ward really comes alive for one hour. In the permanent buildings the wards will be smaller: only six beds in each.

I entered the physiotherapy room expecting to see the same rusty exercise bike and little else, but actually saw a room full of equipment including a treadmill walking machine. With such advanced equipment I knew that there must have been a vast improvement in the quality of treatment, which I later discovered to be true.

Every patient is assessed by each team leader, then the assessments are filed away in an orderly fashion. The nursing notes were still in order so that at any time it was possible to look up information on a certain patient. Theresa had introduced this system since 1990.

Hosneara was at work in the physio room. It was great to see her in her home land where she could be my advisor and provide a shoulder to cry on if need be.

I think the biggest change had been in the occupational therapy department, though not all for the better. The display of crafts had increased considerably and on closer inspection it was obvious that the standard had also been improved, but at a cost. Due to an increase in demand much of the patient participation had been lost. The only involvement they have now is in the men sanding the puzzles and the women making woollen pom-poms, whereas two years ago they helped on each stage of the production line.

However, more specific occupational therapy has improved considerably with set groups and a concentration on the activities of daily living. The metal workshop is another place where it is rare to see patients because the staff are too busy churning out five wheelchairs a week. It is sad that the centre has allowed this to happen and in just one closing chapter I cannot begin to try to explain why it has, other than to put forward the idea that maybe the centre has grown too quickly. The staff are still trying to overcome teething problems, which are only to be expected after such a major move.

Moving away from the buildings I ventured down to the pond, or tank as it is known here and was happily looking for some fish when my I heard lots of people shouting out my name. I looked round and found myself confronted by six patients armed with bows and arrows: I was preventing the keen archers from beginning their game. It was great to see a new project underway and indeed the whole sports section had advanced. Not only did the centre now own the smartest basketball court in the whole country, they also encouraged new sports such as variations on croquet and cricket, hoops and weight-lifting. A sports day was even arranged in which all mobile patients took part - the sense of competitiveness was strong and some good matches were battled out.

The farmyard was impressive with several goats, hens, cows and ducks roaming around between the paddy field and the vegetable plot. Around the back is a field of corn which was donated as a cash crop by an American farmer. The problem was that there was a field of delicious ripe sweetcorn, but no one to eat it. The Bengalis were not interested so in the end the centre sold over five thousand pieces to the large hotels. At the moment one of the centre's fields is rented out, but their long term plans are to develop it into a small village for relatives to stay in. As it lies beyond the boundary wall they could all live a separate life whilst being close enough to be able to learn how to care for their disabled relative once discharged.

It was time for a cup of tea so I joined some patients at the tea shed, which is run by a patient for the centre as a form of training. I managed to get a cup of tea with as little condensed milk as possible and no sugar. This made it not only drinkable, but almost agreeable. There are two shops run by the patients: the other one sells sweet bread, biscuits and fruit, so there is always a snack available for those crucial times of the day when the next meal seems far off in the distance.

There is a basic tin hut on the site which houses four volunteers and becomes the retreat at lunchtimes. Moshuda agreed to cook us a rice meal, in which we indulged ourselves contentedly. I found my accommodation across the field, just five minutes' walk from the centre and from the Savaar Bazaar. I shared it with an Irish nurse who had gone out to Bangladesh for three months to help Theresa on the wards. We both enjoyed bartering for our vegetables in the market and then concocting meals in our primitive kitchen. Our muesli became a legend enjoyed by many.

In the half-way hut I found Khokon. He had been re-admitted for pressure sores after spending a year at home. Even so, he looked healthy and happy, especially when I found him a game of Connect Four. Two years of no play had not diminished his skill in anyway, for he still beat me every time. Mr Topi joined us for a game too.

Ashraf is now in a wheelchair with healed pressure sores, but still has swollen glands. Still wearing his hat he laughed at being called his old nickname and cheerfully told me that he was finally being discharged after two and a half years.

I recognised another tetraplegic from Farmgate called George. He was actually ready to go home, but being an orphan he had nowhere to go. The centre is providing a roof over his head and hoping to start up a cigarette shop so that he can earn a little money. Jobeda now lives in a small hut with her son, who now attends the local school. Jobeda continues to make clothes for her living.

My role in the centre was mainly based in the occupational therapy department. I overlapped with an Australian occupational therapist by one week, which was just long enough for her to hand over to me some of the projects she had started. Leigh had managed to pump some life into the department and had worked hard with the tetraplegics who are so often neglected for the simple reason that they can do less than the paraplegics. A morning occupational therapy group was started for them and I continued it with a fair degree of success. For half an hour I used to do an activity with them to encourage movement and social interaction: a firm favourite was painting because it was the messiest.

Theresa then joined us for a teaching session on bladder and bowel control, pressure sores and lifting. It was in this group that we assessed how each individual could cope with the daily activities of living by getting them to practice cleaning their teeth or dressing themselves. Their progress was recorded on a chart above their beds so that no helper ever gave unnecessary assistance.

There was still plenty of time left in the mornings to help with making beds, giving bed baths and cutting nails on the ward and I observed a few dressing rounds. I tried to spend some time each day with the bed-bound patients, playing games such as noughts and crosses which had been adapted so that patients with little hand movement could play.

Rashida was an old woman who had a degenerative condition and was looked after almost exclusively by her devoted daughter. Together they worked hard, progressing slowly. Every day I helped Rita to walk her mother up and down the parallel bars and was always thanked by Rashida with a big hug. Patients often needed help to stand or put on callipers or to be lifted, so volunteers like myself were never short of work to do.

Madhab agreed to give me a second chance with Bangla lessons, and in the first one I was pleasantly surprised at how much I had retained. Soon my pride was shattered when I had to acknowledge that my threshold for Bangla is very low, but I struggled on by myself throughout the stay. I don't think I really improved and was certainly put to shame by my fellow volunteers.

The joy of being able to escape from the incessant demanding cries of the patients was great and to be able to do so while still on site was a bonus. Unlike in Farmgate, it was possible to find a quiet spot in the grounds to get away from everyone. Much of this chapter was written sitting under a palm tree overlooking the pond. At times I did miss the comforts of living in the Charles' house in smart Gulshan, but ninety per cent of the time I enjoyed being in a rural setting, partaking in more of Bengali life.

On weekends I went into Dhaka to buy treats like peanut butter or to go to the bank. Getting to Dhaka was always eventful due to the reckless standards of driving. The road to Savaar is the main highway to India, so it is kept in good condition, which encourages fast driving. The number of near-misses were not as many, however, as when Clare and I borrowed a rickshaw for a sponsored six mile ride. We overcame the problem of advancing trees, but the trucks were harder to miss. It was fun going into Dhaka and visiting familiar places, but the best part of the day was getting into a rickety overcrowded bus for the long journey back to Savaar.

Walking past the old centre was a shock. It had been turned into a smart restaurant and keeps the fountain working and the garden looking lush. Eating there felt very strange, as our table was in the main ward where Fozzil's bed had been.

The Mirpur plot has a tin shed on it with six patients living in it under the eye of one Ayah. They are all on their way home, but need some time to adjust. Going out into the community helps them to overcome their difficulties with self-image and the practicalities of just coping in the harsh outside world which was not designed for the disabled. Movements are being made in the right direction throughout the country, though. Two large conferences were held in Dhaka on disability in Bangladesh. Hosneara Madhab and Mohua were involved in creating good publicity for the centre as well as for the disabled population as a whole.

I could write another book on the progress of the centre in the last two years, but I won't. Summing up the immense improvements, minor drawbacks and general doings of CRP is incredibly difficult, but the main message that I want to get across is that there is still a long way to go. Only the first step has been taken, a step in the right direction that must be followed by many more.

This second visit has been very important to me and I hope beneficial to the centre. I look forward to the third in the completed 'dream' centre.

Bibliography

- *Bangladesh, a Travel Survival Kit* by Jose Roleo Santiago
Lonely Planet, 1985

- *Bangladesh at a Glance*
Produced and published by Literature Division,
Chittagong, Bangladesh

- *Spoken Bengali, a Common Sense Method* by Gerry Svedlund,
1971

For those intending to visit Bangladesh the Lonely Planet guide is essential reading before you leave, and the other two are well worth buying once in the country.

Other books from Summersdale

The Student Grub Guide
- Favourite easy recipes from around the world
by Alastair Williams (£4. 95)

The Busker's Guide To Europe
- How to make a fortune from your talents
by Stewart Ferris (£5. 95)

Don't Lean Out Of The Window
- Surviving Europe on a Train
by Paul Bassett and Stewart Ferris (£4. 95)

Watch My Back
- A Bouncer's Story
by Geoff Thompson, (£4. 95)

Available through all good bookshops, or in case of difficulty send cheque or postal order made out to **Summersdale Publishers** to: PO Box 49, Chichester, PO19 4LF, UK. Please add £1 postage and packing if ordering from within the UK, add £3 for overseas orders.

Corinna Thomas was born in Kent and has lived in India, Czecho-slovakia, Iceland, and Bulgaria where her parents worked in the Diplomatic Service. She was educated at Bedales school and University College Hospital, London and is now at St Loye's College of Occupational Therapy, Exeter University. Since an early age Corinna has been involved in voluntary work and fund-raising events. She has travelled extensively throughout Europe, South Asia and Australia. It was during one of these trips that she spent three months working as a volunteer in the Centre for the Rehabilitation of the Paralysed, Bangladesh.